G000024756

PUBLIC HEALTH IN THE 21ST CENTURY

# THE TOBACCO CONTROL ACT AND FDA REVIEW OF NEW TOBACCO PRODUCTS

## SELECTED ASSESSMENTS

### GIA A. CHANCE
### EDITOR

*New York*

Copyright © 2014 by Nova Science Publishers, Inc.

**All rights reserved.** No part of this book may be reproduced, stored in a retrieval system or transmitted in any form or by any means: electronic, electrostatic, magnetic, tape, mechanical photocopying, recording or otherwise without the written permission of the Publisher.

For permission to use material from this book please contact us:
Telephone 631-231-7269; Fax 631-231-8175
Web Site: http://www.novapublishers.com

## NOTICE TO THE READER

The Publisher has taken reasonable care in the preparation of this book, but makes no expressed or implied warranty of any kind and assumes no responsibility for any errors or omissions. No liability is assumed for incidental or consequential damages in connection with or arising out of information contained in this book. The Publisher shall not be liable for any special, consequential, or exemplary damages resulting, in whole or in part, from the readers' use of, or reliance upon, this material. Any parts of this book based on government reports are so indicated and copyright is claimed for those parts to the extent applicable to compilations of such works.

Independent verification should be sought for any data, advice or recommendations contained in this book. In addition, no responsibility is assumed by the publisher for any injury and/or damage to persons or property arising from any methods, products, instructions, ideas or otherwise contained in this publication.

This publication is designed to provide accurate and authoritative information with regard to the subject matter covered herein. It is sold with the clear understanding that the Publisher is not engaged in rendering legal or any other professional services. If legal or any other expert assistance is required, the services of a competent person should be sought. FROM A DECLARATION OF PARTICIPANTS JOINTLY ADOPTED BY A COMMITTEE OF THE AMERICAN BAR ASSOCIATION AND A COMMITTEE OF PUBLISHERS.

Additional color graphics may be available in the e-book version of this book.

**Library of Congress Cataloging-in-Publication Data**

ISBN: 978-1-63321-468-2

*Published by Nova Science Publishers, Inc.* † *New York*

# CONTENTS

# PREFACE

This book highlights some of the provisions of the Tobacco Control Act and provides an assessment of FDA efforts to implement the Tobacco Control Act since it was signed into law.

Chapter 1 - The Family Smoking Prevention and Tobacco Control Act (Tobacco Control Act) became law on June 22, 2009. It gives the Food and Drug Administration (FDA) the authority to regulate the manufacture, distribution, and marketing of tobacco products to protect public health. This overview highlights some of the provisions of the Tobacco Control Act.

Chapter 2 - The Family Smoking Prevention and Tobacco Control Act (Tobacco Control Act) amended the Federal Food, Drug, and Cosmetic Act (FD&C Act) to authorize FDA to oversee the manufacture, marketing, distribution, and sale of regulated tobacco products and protect the public from the harmful effects of tobacco product use. This report, which satisfies the requirements of section 106(a) of the Tobacco Control Act, provides an assessment of FDA efforts to implement the Tobacco Control Act since it was signed into law on June 22, 2009.

Among the major accomplishments achieved in these early years is the creation of the FDA Center for Tobacco Products. This report describes the establishment of the new Center with dedicated tobacco program funding, as authorized by the Tobacco Control Act.

Chapter 3 - In 2009, the Family Smoking Prevention and Tobacco Control Act granted FDA, an agency within the Department of Health and Human Services (HHS), authority to regulate tobacco products such as cigarettes. The act requires that tobacco manufacturers submit information to be reviewed by FDA in order to market new tobacco products and established tobacco user fees to fund FDA's tobacco-related activities. The act represents the first time that FDA has had the authority to regulate tobacco products.

Manufacturers have raised concerns about the progress of CTP, the FDA center established by the act to implement its provisions. GAO was asked to examine CTP's review of new tobacco product submissions, responses to meeting requests, and use of funds. This report examines (1) the status of CTP's reviews of new tobacco product submissions; (2) how CTP responded to manufacturers' and other entities' meeting requests, and the length of time CTP took to hold the meetings; and (3) the extent to which FDA has spent its tobacco user fee funds. GAO analyzed data regarding submissions received by FDA as of January 7, 2013; reviewed data on meeting requests, spending plans, and amounts obligated; and interviewed CTP and tobacco industry officials.

Chapter 4 - This is the Statement of Marcia Crosse, Director, Health Care, Government Accountability Office. Hearing on "'Examining the Implementation of the Tobacco Control Act.'"

In: The Tobacco Control Act ...
Editor: Gia A. Chance

ISBN: 978-1-63321-468-2
© 2014 Nova Science Publishers, Inc.

*Chapter 1*

# OVERVIEW OF THE FAMILY SMOKING PREVENTION AND TOBACCO CONTROL ACT: CONSUMER FACT SHEET[*]

## *Center for Tobacco Products, U.S. Food and Drug Administration*

The Family Smoking Prevention and Tobacco Control Act (Tobacco Control Act) became law on June 22, 2009. It gives the Food and Drug

---

[*] This is an edited, reformatted and augmented version of a document released by the FDA.

Administration (FDA) the authority to regulate the manufacture, distribution, and marketing of tobacco products to protect public health.

# THE TOBACCO CONTROL ACT

- Recognizes that virtually all new users of tobacco products are under 18—the minimum legal age to purchase these products. Many new users will become addicted before they are old enough to understand the risks and ultimately may die too young of tobacco-related diseases. The Tobacco Control Act seeks to, among other things, prevent and reduce tobacco use by young people.
- Recognizes that tobacco products are legal products available for adult use, prohibits false or misleading labeling and advertising for tobacco products and provides the tobacco industry with several mechanisms to submit an application to FDA for new products or tobacco products with modified risk claims.
- Gives FDA enforcement authority as well as a broad set of sanctions for violations of the law and directs FDA to contract with states to assist FDA with retailer inspections.

This overview highlights some of the provisions of the Tobacco Control Act and is not intended to be a comprehensive guide or to reflect FDA's interpretation of the Tobacco Control Act. For complete information, you must read the entire law. For your convenience, in the text below we provide the section number of the Tobacco Control Act.

# WHAT THE TOBACCO CONTROL ACT DOES

*Restricts cigarettes and smokeless tobacco retail sales to youth by directing FDA to issue regulations which, among other things:*

- Require proof of age to purchase these tobacco products – the federal minimum age to purchase is 18—Sec. 102
- Require face-to-face sales, with certain exemptions for vending machines and self-service displays in adult-only facilities—Sec. 102

- Ban the sale of packages of fewer than 20 cigarettes—Sec. 102

*Restricts tobacco product advertising and marketing to youth by directing FDA to issue regulations which, among other things:*

- Limit color and design of packaging and advertisements, including audio-visual advertisements— Sec. 102 (However, implementation of this provision is uncertain due to pending litigation. See *Discount Tobacco City & Lottery v. USA,* formerly *Commonwealth Brands v. FDA.*)
- Ban tobacco product sponsorship of sporting or entertainment events under the brand name of cigarettes or smokeless tobacco—Sec.102
- Ban free samples of cigarettes and brand-name non-tobacco promotional items—Sec. 102

Note: Among its many provisions, the Tobacco Control Act required FDA to reissue its 1996 final regulations aimed at restricting the sale and distribution of cigarette and smokeless tobacco products.– Sec. 102.

The Tobacco Control Act specifically:

- Prohibits "reduced harm" claims including "light," "low," or "mild," without an FDA order to allow marketing—Sec. 911 of the *Federal Food, Drug, and Cosmetic Act* (FDCA)
- Requires industry to submit marketing research documents—Sec. 904 of the FDCA

*Requires bigger, more prominent warning labels for cigarettes and smokeless tobacco products:*

(However, the implementation date of more prominent warning labels for cigarettes is uncertain, due to ongoing proceedings in the case of *R. J. Reynolds Tobacco Co. v. U.S. Food and Drug Administration*, No, 11-1482 (D.D.C.), *on appeal*, No, 11-5332 (D.C.Cir.).)

- Packaging and advertisements for cigarettes and smokeless tobacco must have revised warning labels with a larger font size. Font colors are limited to white on a black background or black on a white background.—Sec. 201 and 204
- Cigarette package health warnings will be required to cover the top 50 percent of both the front and rear panels of the package, and the nine

specific warning messages must be equally and randomly displayed and distributed in all areas of the United States. These messages must be accompanied by color graphics showing the negative health consequences of smoking cigarettes.—Sec. 201

- Smokeless tobacco package warnings must cover 30 percent of the two principal display panels, and the four specific required messages must be equally and randomly displayed and distributed in all areas of the United States.—Sec. 204

*Gives FDA authority over, among other things:*

- Registration and inspection of tobacco companies—Sec. 905 of the FDCA
  - Requires owners and operators of tobacco companies to register annually and be subject to inspection every 2 years by FDA.
- Standards for tobacco products—Sec. 907 of the FDCA
  - Allows FDA to require standards for tobacco products (for example, tar and nicotine levels) as appropriate to protect public health.
  - Bans cigarettes with characterizing flavors (except menthol and tobacco).
- "Premarket Review" of new tobacco products—Sec. 910 and 905 of the FDCA
  - Requires manufacturers who wish to market a new tobacco product to obtain a marketing order from FDA prior to marketing that new product.
- "Modified risk" products—Sec. 911 of the FDCA
  - Requires manufacturers who wish to market a tobacco product with a claim of reduced harm to obtain a marketing order from FDA.
- Enforcement action plan for advertising and promotion restrictions— Sec. 105 > FDA published a document entitled "Enforcement Action Plan for Promotion and Advertising Restrictions." > The action plan details FDA's current thinking on how it intends to enforce certain requirements under the Tobacco Control Act.

## THE TOBACCO CONTROL ACT ALSO REQUIRES

- Tobacco industry must disclose research on the health, toxicological, behavioral, or physiologic effects of tobacco use.—Sec. 904 of the FDCA
- Tobacco industry must disclose information on ingredients and constituents in tobacco products, and must notify FDA of any changes.—Sec. 904 of the FDCA

## HOW FDA OVERSEES THE IMPLEMENTATION OF THE TOBACCO CONTROL ACT

Among other things, FDA:

- Established the Center for Tobacco Products to implement the Tobacco Control Act—Sec. 901 of the FDCA
- Established the Tobacco Products Scientific Advisory Committee to provide advice, information, and recommendations to the FDA—Sec. 917 of the FDCA
- Assesses user fees on tobacco product manufacturers and importers based on their market share. The fees are used to fund FDA activities related to the regulation of tobacco products—Sec. 919 of the FDCA
- Reports to Congress on how best to encourage companies to develop innovative products that help people stop smoking—Sec. 918 of the FDCA
- Issues regulations and conducts inspections to investigate illicit trade in tobacco products—Sec. 920 of the FDCA
- Convenes a panel of experts to study the public health implications of raising the minimum age to purchase tobacco products—Sec. 104

Limits on FDA's authority FDA cannot:

- Ban certain specified classes of tobacco products—Sec. 907 of the FDCA
- Require the reduction of nicotine yields to zero—Sec. 907 of the FDCA

- Require prescriptions to purchase tobacco products—Sec. 906 of the FDCA
- Ban face-to-face tobacco sales in any particular category of retail outlet—Sec. 906 of the FDCA

The Tobacco Control Act preserves the authority of state, local, and tribal governments to regulate tobacco products in certain specific respects. It also prohibits, with certain exceptions, state and local requirements that are different from, or in addition to, requirements under the provisions of the FDCA relating to specified areas.

For more information visit www.fda.gov/TobaccoControlAct.

In: The Tobacco Control Act ...          ISBN: 978-1-63321-468-2
Editor: Gia A. Chance          © 2014 Nova Science Publishers, Inc.

*Chapter 2*

# PROGRESS AND EFFECTIVENESS OF THE IMPLEMENTATION OF THE FAMILY SMOKING PREVENTION AND TOBACCO CONTROL ACT*

## *U.S. Food and Drug Administration*

## EXECUTIVE SUMMARY

The Family Smoking Prevention and Tobacco Control Act (Tobacco Control Act) amended the Federal Food, Drug, and Cosmetic Act (FD&C Act) to authorize FDA to oversee the manufacture, marketing, distribution, and sale of regulated tobacco products and protect the public from the harmful effects of tobacco product use. This report, which satisfies the requirements of section 106(a) of the Tobacco Control Act, provides an assessment of FDA efforts to implement the Tobacco Control Act since it was signed into law on June 22, 2009.

Among the major accomplishments achieved in these early years is the creation of the FDA Center for Tobacco Products. This report describes the establishment of the new Center with dedicated tobacco program funding, as authorized by the Tobacco Control Act.

---

* This is an edited, reformatted and augmented version of a Report to Congress, dated May 23, 2013.

Other key accomplishments include:

- Establishing an initial framework for industry registration, product listing, and disclosure of ingredients and ham1ful and potentially harmful constituents in tobacco products and tobacco smoke.
- Pursuant to the FD&C Act, requiring cigarette, roll-your-own, and smokeless tobacco product manufacturers to seek FDA authorization before marketing a new product or making changes to existing products.
- Enforcing the statute's prohibition on the use of marketing terms for regulated tobacco products that imply reduced risk (such as "light," "mild," or "low") without FDA authorization.
- Developing a process for the review and evaluation of applications for new tobacco products and modified risk tobacco products.
- Implementing the statute's ban on cigarettes with certain characterizing flavors.
- Increasing regulatory science capabilities through research to better understand regulated tobacco products and patterns of tobacco use.
- Restricting access and marketing of cigarettes and smokeless tobacco products to youth.
- Implementing a compliance and enforcement program to ensure industry compliance with regulatory requirements.
- Establishing public education campaigns about the dangers of regulated tobacco products.

As required by the Tobacco Control Act, the report also describes impediments to progress during this time and provides data on certain tobacco product applications as well as on the number of full time equivalents (FTEs) engaged in implementing the FDA tobacco program.

# I. OVERVIEW

Tobacco use is the single most preventable cause of disease, disability, and death in the United States. Each year, an estimated 443,000 Americans die prematurely from smoking or exposure to secondhand smoke; more than the number of deaths due to alcohol, illegal drug use, homicide, suicide, car accidents, and HIV/AIDS combined.[1] Approximately 8.6 million people in the United States live with a serious illness caused by smoking.[2]

In 2009, President Obama signed into law the Family Smoking Prevention and Tobacco Control Act (Tobacco Control Act), which amended the Federal Food, Drug, and Cosmetic Act (FD&C Act or the Act), granting authority to the U.S. Food and Drug Administration (FDA) to regulate tobacco products. This new authority gave FDA comprehensive tools to protect the public from the hamlful effects of tobacco use, including thorough science-based regulation of the manufacturing, marketing, and distribution of tobacco products.

FDA was given immediate authority to regulate cigarettes, cigarette tobacco, roll-your-own tobacco, and smokeless tobacco. For the American public this means, among other things:

- New tobacco products of these types cannot come on the market without FDA review, which includes consideration of the potential public health impact;
- Products can no longer be marketed as reduced risk or reduced haml without scientific evidence showing both that they reduce harm and the risk of disease to individual users and that marketing them would benefit the population as a whole; and
- Access to new information about the harmful and potentially harmful constituents of these tobacco products and tobacco smoke.

The Tobacco Control Act also authorizes FDA to deem other tobacco products to be subject to FDA's regulatory authority in Chapter IX of the Food, Drug, and Cosmetic Act (FD&C Act). FDA publicly announced in the Unified Agenda of January 8, 2013, that it will issue a proposed rule to deem products that meet the statutory definition of a "tobacco product," which includes "any product made or derived from tobacco that is intended for human consumption" that is not a drug, device, or combination product under the FD&C Act, to be subject to FDA's regulatory authority in Chapter IX.[3] All newly-deemed tobacco products would automatically be subject to certain provisions in the FD&C Act, such as registration, product listing, ingredient listing, user fees for certain products, and the adulteration and misbranding provisions of the statute.

This report satisfies the requirements of Section 106(a) of the Tobacco Control Act, which states:

Not later than 3 years[4] after the date of enactment of this Act, and not less than evely 2 years thereafter, the Secretary of Health and Human Services shall submit to the Committee on Health, Education, Labor, and Pensions of the Senate and the Committee on Energy and Commerce of the House of Representatives, a report concerning-

(I) the progress of the Food and Drug Administration in implementing this division, including major accomplishments, objective measurements of progress, and the identification of any areas that have not been fully implemented;

(2) impediments identified by the Food and Drug Administration to progress in implementing this division and to meeting statutory time frames;

(3) data on the number of new product applications received under section 910 of the Federal Food, Drug, and Cosmetic Act and modified risk product applications received under section 911 of such Act, and the number of applications acted on under each category: and

(4) data on the number of full time equivalents engaged in implementing this division.

## II. PROGRESS OF THE FDA IN IMPLEMENTING THE FAMILY SMOKING PREVENTION AND TOBACCO CONTROL ACT

FDA's first priority following the passage of the Tobacco Control Act was creating the Center for Tobacco Products (CTP), FDA's first new center in 21 years. CTP oversees the implementation of the FDA tobacco program, pursuant to the Tobacco Control Act. The Center has been tasked with developing the scientific, regulatory, and public education infrastructure necessary to implement and track FDA's goals for reducing the haml s associated with tobacco products, preventing initiation of tobacco use, particularly among youth, and encouraging cessation so that more Americans stop using tobacco products. Key objectives involved in launching CTP included recruiting talented officials to lead the center, hiring skilled staff, setting up necessary infrastructure and technology resources, and putting in place processes to meet statutory deadlines and directives.

## Establishing the Center for Tobacco Products

The Tobacco Control Act authorized FDA to use appropriated funds during fiscal year (FY) 2009 for the initial start-up costs of tobacco regulation activities. In the last quarter of FY 2009, CTP began collecting user fees authorized under the FD&C Act to fund the agency's tobacco regulation activities. The Tobacco Control Act stipulates that these user fees may only be spent for FDA tobacco regulation activities. Conversely, the law provides that no funds, other than these user fees, may be spent on FDA tobacco regulation activities.

Section 919 of the Act identifies the total dollar amount of user fees authorized to be assessed and collected each year, on a quarterly basis, from tobacco manufacturers and importers. Tobacco user fees are "no year" funds and may be carried over from one fiscal year to the next. Fees are allocated among classes of regulated tobacco products, currently cigarettes, snuff, chewing tobacco, and roll-your-own tobacco[5], based on the volume of the different tobacco product classes reported to the U.S. Depal1ment of Treasury's Bureau of Alcohol, Tobacco Tax and Trade for excise tax purposes. Under a memorandum of understanding, the U.S. Department of Agriculture (USDA) has been providing FDA with the infomlation on percentage market share by class of tobacco product and by individual company within each tobacco product class. Utilizing information received from USDA, FDA is able to assess user fees as directed by section 919 of the Tobacco Control Act for individual domestic manufacturers and importers based on their respective market share in each tobacco product class.[6] As of February 28, 2013, 99 percent of user fees assessed were being collected from manufacturers and importers.

During its start-up phase, FDA established the regulatory framework and staffing foundation to begin tobacco product regulation. All statutory obligations were met and recruitment and hiring proceeded as projected. It is important to note that full use of existing unexpended balances was planned for by the agency. The agency is required to continue to build the scientific base for tobacco product regulation and to fully implement the Tobacco Control Act. For example, now that much of the foundational work has been completed, FDA's tobacco program obligations in FY 2013 have been aggressive. As of February 28, 2013, the agency has obligated 63 percent of its spending plan ($540 million) and is on target to fully obligate its FY 2013 planned level of $847 million.

## Hiring CTP's Director and Deputy Director

After a national search, Dr. Lawrence Deyton, M.D., M.S.P.H., was selected as CTP's founding Director in September 2009. Dr. Deyton is an expert on public health, tobacco use, and veterans' health issues, and is a clinical professor of medicine and health policy at George Washington University School of Medicine and Health Sciences. Prior to joining FDA, Dr. Deyton was Chief Public Health and Environmental Hazards Officer for the U.S. Department of Veterans Affairs. He also served in leadership positions in the National Institute of Allergy and Infectious Diseases at the National Institutes of Health (NIH).

In March 2013, Dr. Deyton was succeeded by Mitchell Zeller, J.D. Mr. Zeller has been working on FDA issues for more than 30 years, including seven years as the Associate Commissioner and Director of the FDA's Office of Tobacco Programs from 1993 to 2000. Mr. Zeller has also served as the Executive Vice President of the American Legacy Foundation, which was created out of the 1998 Master Settlement Agreement to address the health effects of tobacco use. He also has prior experience as a public interest attorney and a congressional counsel.

In June 2012, FDA Commissioner Margaret A. Hamburg, M.D. named Richard J. Turman as CTP's Deputy Director. Prior to joining CTP, Mr. Turman served as the Principal Deputy Assistant Secretary for Financial Resources at the U.S. Department of Health and Human Services (HHS) and as the Associate Director for Budget at NIH.

The priorities of the Center Director and Deputy Director include expanding effective communications across FDA and CTP, within HHS, and among stakeholders on matters related to tobacco product regulation and FDA's regulatory authorities, as well as advancing HHS's tobacco-related goals.

## Staffing the Center

After filling the leadership positions in CTP, the center mew from a handful to hundreds of employees dedicated to protecting public health, including regulatory counsels, policy analysts, scientists, researchers, management officers, communications specialists, and other professionals needed to design and implement a comprehensive program of tobacco product regulation as required by the FD&C Act.

The following table displays full-time equivalent (FTE) program levels from FY 2009 through FY 2013.[7]

| Fiscal Year | Program Level FTE |
|---|---|
| 2009 Actual | 0[8] |
| 2010 Actual | 113 |
| 2011 Actual | 256 |
| 2012 Actual | 426 |
| 2013 Request | 546 |

## Objective Measures of Progress

In the four years since the enactment of the Tobacco Control Act, FDA has made significant progress developing a framework for tobacco product regulation that is designed to reduce the impact of tobacco on public health, to keep people, especially our nation's youth, from starting to use tobacco, and to make it easier for current consumers who wish to quit. For example, FDA has published 8 rules and regulatory documents and 24 guidance and draft guidance documents related to tobacco products, a complete listing can be found in Appendix A.

Other key accomplishments include:

- Establishing an initial framework for industry registration, product listing, and disclosure of ingredients and harmful and poten6ally harmful constituents (HPHCs) in tobacco products and tobacco smoke.
- Pursuant to the FD&C Act, requiring cigarette, roll-your-own, and smokeless tobacco product manufacturers to seek FDA authorization before marketing a new product or making changes to existing products.
- Implementing and enforcing the statute's prohibition on the use of marketing terms for regulated tobacco products that imply reduced risk (such as "light," "mild," or "low") without FDA authorization.
- Developing a process for the review and evaluation of applications for new products, modified risk, and substantially equivalent tobacco products.
- Implementing and enforcing the statute's ban on cigarettes with certain characterizing flavors.

- Increasing regulatory science capabilities through research to better understand regulated products and patterns of tobacco use.
- Restricting access and marketing of cigarettes and smokeless tobacco products to youth.
- Implementing a compliance and enforcement program to ensure industry compliance with regulatory requirements.
- Establishing public education campaigns about the dangers of regulated tobacco products.

These accomplishments demonstrate the commitment of FDA to exercise its new regulatory authority under the FD&C Act to effectively regulate the manufacture, marketing, and distribution of tobacco products and to advance tobacco product regulations appropriate for the protection of public health.

## III. THE REGULATORY FRAMEWORK FOR TOBACCO PRODUCTS

As the regulatory framework for tobacco products continues to evolve, FDA has set forth comprehensive objectives to:

1. Understand the regulated products.
2. Review new products and product changes to protect public health.
3. Prohibit false, misleading, and unsubstantiated product claims that state or imply reduced risk.
4. Decrease the banns of tobacco products.
5. Expand the science base for regulatory action.
6. Restrict marketing and distribution to protect public health.
7. Ensure industry compliance with FDA regulations.
8. Educate the public.

FDA's progress toward achieving these core framework objectives is discussed in detail below.

## 1. Understand the Regulated Products

The FD&C Act, as amended by the Tobacco Control Act, empowers FDA to build knowledge of regulated tobacco products. In pali, this is accomplished through three specific reporting requirements. First, companies must register manufacturing facilities and provide a list of all their regulated products.[9] To assist industry with compliance, FDA issued a final guidance document in November 2009. [10] Second, companies are required to provide a list of all ingredients for regulated products.[11] To assist companies with this requirement, FDA published a final guidance in December 2009 detailing procedures for submitting ingredient information, including what information to submit, how information should be submitted, and when it is appropriate to do so. [12]

Third, the FD&C Act directs FDA to establish and peliodically revise a list of HPHCs in tobacco products and requires all tobacco product manufacturers to measure and report HPHC quantities to FDA by brand and subbrand.[13] HPHCs are those constituents in a tobacco product or tobacco smoke that are, or have the potential to be inhaled, ingested, or absorbed into the body and that cause or have the potential to cause direct or indirect harm to users or non-users of tobacco products.[14]

In developing the HPHC list, FDA solicited input and recommendations from the FDA's Tobacco Products Scientific Advisory Committee. FDA also released a list of HPHCs for public comment[15] before establishing a list of these constituents in April 2012.[16] The established list, is available in Appendix B, and identifies 93 HPHCs. The list also identifies each constituent with one of the following disease effects: cancer, cardiovascular disease, respiratory effects, developmental or reproductive effects, and addiction. In April 2012, FDA also released a draft guidance document for industry related to the reporting of HPHCs.[17]

A provision in the Tobacco Control Act requires FDA to publicly display infomlation about HPHCs, including the amount of each chemical present in specific brands and sub-brands of tobacco products, in a way that is understandable and not misleading to the public by April 1, 2013.[18] FDA intends to make such detailed information about chemicals in tobacco products and tobacco smoke available, but only when the agency can assure the public that the information released is understandable and not misleading. Therefore, FDA is not releasing any information at this time. Currently, the agency is evaluating the data it has received from manufacturers and will be conducting rigorous scientific studies to ensure that the required information is presented in a way that is understandable and not misleading to the public. When FDA completes these important activities, the agency will be in a position to publish the required information consistent with the statutory requirements. By doing so, FDA will help consumers make more infomled decisions about tobacco products.

Under Section 901 of the FD&C Act, products currently regulated by FDA under Chapter IX of the FD&C Act, include: cigarettes, cigarette tobacco, roll-your-own tobacco, and smokeless tobacco. In addition, FDA is authorized to deem, by regulation, other tobacco products to be subject to this Chapter. FDA has publicly announced its intention to deem products that meet the statutory definition of "tobacco product," which is "any product made or derived from tobacco that is intended for human consumption, including any component, part, or accessory of a tobacco product" that is not a drug, device, or combination product under the FD&C Act.[19]

## 2. Review New Products and Product Changes to Protect Public Health

Historically, tobacco manufacturers regularly altered characteristics of their products to improve taste, appeal to new users, and retain current users as their preferences change. The FD&C Act authorizes FDA's regulation of tobacco products to protect public health by requiring manufacturers to seek FDA authorization before marketing a new product, including making changes to an existing product. Section 910 of the Act defines a "new" tobacco product as a product not commercially marketed in the United States as of February 15, 2007, or a product already on the market that is modified after that date.[20] This premarket review process gives FDA the ability to ensure that the marketing of any new product, including a modified product, is appropriate for the protection of public health and allows for greater awareness and understanding of the changes being made to tobacco products.

Under the premarket review process, there are three ways a new tobacco product, including an existing product that is modified, can obtain FDA authorization for distribution or retail sale: a premarket tobacco product application; an application demonstrating substantial equivalence (SE) to certain commercially marketed products; or an application for exemption from demonstrating SE.

## *Premarket Tobacco Product Applications*

One pathway for a new tobacco product to receive market authorization is through the Premarket Tobacco Product Application (PMTA) process.[21] In September 2011, FDA issued a draft guidance document about PMT A submissions describing what the FD&C Act requires to be submitted in a new tobacco product application.[22] The draft guidance also sought comment on the infomlation to be included in the application that the agency would use to detemline whether the marketing of a new tobacco product is appropriate for the protection of the public health, as determined with respect to the risks and benefits to the population as a whole, including users and non-users of tobacco products, and taking into account the impact on cessation and initiation.

## *Demonstrating Substantial Equivalence to Certain Commercially Marketed Products*

Demonstrating SE to a product already on the market is a second pathway to marketing authorization under specific circumstances. Under the SE pathway, whenever an existing tobacco product is modified, the manufacturer must submit a report with sufficient scientific data and information to FDA to demonstrate that the product characteristics,[23] as compared to the predicate product are the same,[24] or the tobacco product has different characteristics but does not raise different questions of public health.[25]

Pursuant to Section 910(a)(2)(B) of the Act, products that were first introduced or delivered for introduction into interstate commerce for commercial distribution between February 15, 2007, and March 22, 2011, and for which SE reports were submitted plior to March 23, 2011, can remain on the market unless FDA issues an order that they are "not substantially equivalent (NSE)." FDA refers to these SE reports as "provisional." An SE report for a tobacco product not covered by this provision is considered a "regular" report and the product covered by the application cannot be marketed unless FDA first issues an order finding the product substantially equivalent and in compliance with the FD&C Act. FDA issued a guidance document in January 2011 describing the content and data to be included in the report and the process for its review.[26]

## *Exemption from Demonstrating Substantial Equivalence*

The third pathway for new tobacco products is a request for an exemption from the SE requirements. This pathway is available for products modified by the addition or deletion of an additive or a change in the quantity of an existing additive, if:

- FDA finds the modification to be minor;
- FDA determines an SE report is not necessary to ensure that permitting the tobacco product to be marketed would be appropriate for the protection of public health; and
- an exemption is otherwise appropliate.[27]

In July 2011, FDA issued a final rule on "Exemptions from Substantial Equivalence Requirements"[28] that established the procedures for requesting an SE exemption.

### Status of New Product Applications under Section 910

FDA review of a new product, including a modified product, requires scientific and technical expertise in order to assess how the product design, ingredients, and other characteristics impact the public health. As of February 28, 2013, FDA had not received any premarket applications for new tobacco products and has focused its review efforts on applications seeking to demonstrate SE.

### Process for Review of Substantial Equivalence Reports

At this time, regular SE submissions are reviewed in the order they are received, and provisional SE submissions receive a Public Health Impact (PHI) Review, in which applications are given a tier assignment (1-4). Those with a tier 1 assignment, indicating the highest potential negative public health impact, are the first provisional applications to be reviewed. The PHI review process was necessary because over 3,000 provisional applications arrived within a short span of time prior to the March 23, 2011, filing deadline.

The review for an SE report involves a stepped process in order to ensure consistency, transparency, and predictability. FDA first performs a Jurisdictional Review to determine whether the product is currently subject to regulation as a tobacco product. FDA then carries out a Completeness Review to determine if the report is administratively complete. If additional infomlation is needed, FDA sends an Administrative Advice and Information (AI) Request letter to the applicant requesting specific information.

After this review, FDA performs a Predicate Tobacco Product Eligibility Determination, which is the process for evaluating whether the proposed predicate tobacco product (the tobacco product to which the proposed new tobacco product is being compared in the SE Report) meets the FD&C Act criteria to be a predicate. FDA currently prioritizes predicate reviews for regular SE submissions since the products covered in a regular SE submission are not authorized to be commercially marketed unless FDA issues an order of substantial equivalence.

FDA performs a Scientific Review of SE submissions to assess the chemistry, toxicology, engineeling, and other appropriate scientific propeliies of the tobacco product and determines whether its characteristics are the same as the predicate product or if there are different characteristics, and whether the new product raises different questions of public health. If additional scientific information is needed, FDA sends a Scientific AI letter to the applicant requesting specific information and asking the applicant to respond within 60 days. FDA completes the scientific review upon receipt of that infomlation or seeks further clarification as needed. Before making a determination that a product is SE or NSE, FDA must determine whether any other additional information is needed. FDA then makes its determination and communicates the determination to the applicant.

As of February 28, 2013, FDA had received a total of 4,321 submissions seeking to demonstrate SE to a predicate product, including, 3,544 ·'provisional" submissions that were received before March 23, 2011, and apply to products already marketed in the United States. The remaining 777 applications are "regular'· submissions for products not currently on the market.

FDA has completed Jurisdictional Reviews for 3,782 of the 4,253 SE submissions. FDA has conducted Completeness Reviews for 2,638 SE submissions. FDA has perfomled a PHI review and provided a tier assignment (1-4) for 3,440 provisional SE reports. FDA has completed Predicate Tobacco Product Eligibility Determinations for 175 regular SE submissions. Of the 4,321 SE submissions received, 69 were withdrawn by the applicants. Manufacturers may withdraw an SE application at any time in the SE review process if they are not able to meet FDA's regulatory standards, or for other business reasons.

In addition, as of February 28, 2013, FDA had received and acknowledged 28 submissions seeking exemption from the SE reporting requirements; these are now under review. FDA had also received 530 requests by manufacturers for verification that a product was commercially marketed in the United States as of February 15, 2007, and not only in a test market. Of these, FDA has provided verification for 315 requests and three requests were withdrawn by the companies.

There are many factors that can affect the timing of a determination by FDA, including the completeness of an application or whether there is a need for manufacturers to submit more information or provide an additional explanation so that FDA can complete its assessment. It is important to note that there was a wide range of quality in SE reports submitted thus far by the tobacco industry, which is new to FDA regulation. In almost all cases, reports that have been submitted lack both information referenced in FDA guidance documents to facilitate FDA review and information required for FDA to make its determination.

Examples of some of the general issues that FDA is observing across multiple applicants include:

- Reports containing contradictory statements, particularly about whether the product characteristics were the same or different;
  Reports naming an unacceptable predicate product;
- Reports lacking infomlation to completely understand product composition, including infomlation about the tobacco blend used in the product;
- Reports missing specifications on components used in the manufacture of the finished product;
- Reports with HPHC measurements that were scientifically inadequate or did not include infomlation needed to evaluate data quality; and
- Reports in which information on product design was incomplete, preventing a scientific assessment.

In response to industry feedback, where possible, FDA is streamlining the SE review process:

- FDA increased opportunities for communication with industry by encouraging teleconferences between the assigned FDA regulatory project manager and the submitter.
- FDA has taken steps to facilitate quicker responses to questions.
- FDA modified the initial review for completeness to focus only on administrative issues, so that applicants can be notified more quickly about submission deficiencies.
- FDA hosted webinars for tobacco manufacturers specifically to discuss the types of information that the agency needs to complete the review of SE reports.
- On September 22, 2011, FDA issued a draft guidance document with responses to frequently asked questions about demonstrating SE of a new tobacco product.

- FDA launched a new section on its website: *Tobacco Product Review and Evaluation* providing comprehensive infomlation on the pathways available to legally market new tobacco products, including SE.

FDA is committed to carefully and thoroughly reviewing all submission s in order to protect the public health as required by the FD&C Act. FDA is also committed to a consistent, transparent, and predictable review process and to completing reviews of all new product applications in a timely manner.[29]

## 3. Prohibit False/Misleading/Unsubstantiated Product Claims That State or Imply Modified Risk

A regulated tobacco product may not be distributed or marketed with any statement or claim (expressed or implied) about reduced lisk or harm associated with the product, unless the manufacturer demonstrates, and FDA finds that the product, as actually used, will significantly reduce harm and risk to users and will benefit the health of the population as a whole, taking into account both users of tobacco products and persons who do not currently use tobacco products.[30] In certain circumstances where scientific infolmation is not available and cannot be made available without conducting long-teml epidemiological studies and certain statutory criteria are met, an "exposure modification order'' may be issued. Such an order requires a finding that the product reduces or eliminates exposure to a substance for which the available scientific evidence suggests that a measurable and substantial reduction in morbidity and mortality is reasonably likely to be demonstrated in future studies. These requirements seek to prevent false, misleading and unsubstantiated product claims about the safety or relative harmfulness of tobacco products.

A draft guidance was released for public comment in March 2012 for those manufacturers that seek to market a modified risk tobacco product (MR TP), which is defined as "any tobacco product that is sold or distributed for use to reduce harm or the risk of tobacco-related disease associated with commercially marketed tobacco products."[31] The draft guidance for MRTP applications provides recommendations on how to organize, submit, and file an application, what scientific studies and analyses to submit, and what information to collect through post-market surveillance and studies if an FDA order permitting the marketing of the product is issued.[32] FDA has been meeting with manufacturers to discuss studies the manufacturers have proposed to provide the scientific evidence needed to demonstrate that marketing of a modified risk product will significantly reduce harm and risk of tobacco-related disease to individual tobacco users and benefits the health of the population as a whole. As of February 28, 2013, no MRTP applications had been filed with FDA.

Additionally, Section 911 of the FD&C Act specifically prohibits the use of the descriptors "light," "mild," or "low" or similar terms in regulated tobacco product labeling without an FDA order allowing the descriptors to be used. FDA issued a guidance document in June 2010 for industry about the use of "light," "mild," "low," or similar descriptors with respect to regulated products.[33] As of February 28, 2013, FDA has issued 65 Warning Letters that include charges related to the prohibition of "low," "light," or "mild" descriptors on regulated tobacco products under section 911 of the FD&C Act. In addition, FDA has sought Civil Money Penalties in two cases for tobacco product retailers violating the prohibition on the use of "low," "light," or "mild" descriptors on regulated tobacco products. FDA regularly updates its Health Fraud webpage to highlight these Warning Letters and promote public awareness of the illegal use of "light," "mild," and "low" claims for tobacco products that do not have an FDA order permitting such claims. In addition, FDA has conducted webinars, which included an overview of the requirements of the FD&C Act, Warning Letters issued, and violations cited under section 911 of the FD&C Act, to help educate the public and to encourage voluntary compliance by regulated industry.

## 4. Decrease the Harms of Tobacco Products

The FD&C Act directs FDA to prevent and reduce the banns caused by regulated tobacco products by, among other authorities, issuing tobacco product standards if the agency finds it appropliate for the protection of the public health. Section 907(a)(3) of the Act allows FDA to develop such product standards with consideration of scientific evidence concerning the risks and benefits to the population as a whole, including users and nonusers, and the likely impacts on cessation for existing users of tobacco products and initiation for nonusers. Examples given in the FD&C Act of the types of product standards that FDA might issue include provisions related to nicotine yields, levels of harmful constituents, and product construction and properties.[34]

In addition, FDA is enforcing the special rule in Section 907(a)(l)(a) of the FD&C Act that prohibits cigarettes with celiain characterizing flavors, such as candy and fruit, in order to address their appeal to youth. In June 2010, Indonesia brought a challenge, under the World Trade Organization (WTO) dispute settlement procedures, regarding the Tobacco Control Act ban on certain characterizing flavors and the process by which it was implemented. One of Indonesia's central claims was that the provision breached the U.S. obligation to provide national treatment in that it provides less favorable treatment to an imported Indonesian product (clove cigarettes) than to a "like" domestic product (menthol cigarettes). In April 2012, the WTO Appellate Body affirmed a dispute settlement panel's findings that the provision breached the United States' national treatment obligation under the WTO Agreement. Under WTO rules, the United States and Indonesia agreed that the "reasonable period of time" for the United States to come into compliance with the WTO rulings would expire on July 24, 2013.[35] The statutory ban on characterizing flavors remains in effect.

## 5. Expand the Science Base for Regulatory Action

A strong science base is a key underpinning of the tobacco regulatory framework and FDA's ability to develop guidance and regulations, and to review product applications.

To further develop a comprehensive science base to inform effective tobacco product regulation, HHS has prioritized the establishment of a research program to cover a broad array of scientific questions that might impact tobacco regulatory decisions.[36] Within FDA, CTP is tasked with using the science that is currently available and carrying out new research that will drive tobacco regulatory action based on the best available science.

In order to carry out this task, CTP has initiated the development of a research program to inform future regulatory options and meet directives in the FD&C Act. CTP is reviewing relevant scientific literature to identify research gaps related to the regulation of tobacco products, and priority research questions were elicited from various stakeholders. The resulting research questions were categorized into seven broad areas: [37]

- Diversity of tobacco products;
- Reducing addiction ;
- Reducing toxicity and carcinogenicity;
- Adverse health consequences;
- Communications;
- Marketing of tobacco products; and
- Economics and policies.

Underscored within these research areas is the need to address vulnerable populations since both the use of tobacco products and the resulting adverse health outcomes impact different populations in different ways. Population s of interest include people with mental health or medical co-morbidities, the military/veterans, the lesbian, gay, bi-sexual, transgendered, questioning (LGBTQ) community, and pregnant women/women of reproductive age. There are also a series of potential contributing factors including age, gender, race, ethnicity, income, occupation, and geographic location.

To advance these research priorities, FDA has embarked on collaborations and awarded contracts to fund research with other government agencies, non-government science research organizations and academic institutions.

### Tobacco Products Scientific Advisory Committee

The FD&C Act mandated that FDA establish a 12-member Tobacco Products Scientific Advisory Committee (TPSAC) to provide appropriate advice, information and recommendations to the Secretary of HHS and the FDA Commissioner. The committee's members and the Chair were selected by the Secretary, as per the Act, from among individuals technically qualified by training and experience in the fields of medicine, medical ethics, science, or technology involving the manufacture, evaluation, or use of tobacco products and who are of appropriate diversified professional backgrounds. The Committee shall be composed of 7 health care professionals; 1 officer/employee of a state, local or federal government; 1 representative of the general public; 1 representative of the tobacco manufacturing industry; 1 representative of small business tobacco manufacturing industry; and 1 representative of tobacco growers. Members serve for terms of up to four years.[38]

The TPSAC is directed to provide advice, information, and recommendations on tobacco-related topics, including: the effects of the alteration of nicotine yields from tobacco products, whether there is a threshold level below which nicotine yields do not produce dependence on the tobacco product involved, and other issues as requested by the Secretary. FDA is required to refer to TPSAC, and TPSAC is required to review, any application filed by a manufacturer for a modified risk tobacco product and may review, among other things, other premarket tobacco product applications and petitions filed by a manufacturer for exemption from requirements relating to good manufacturing practices.

Specific TPSAC reports and recommendations required by the FD&C Act include the impact of the use of menthol in cigarettes on the public health, including such use among children, African Americans, Hispanics and other racial and ethnic minorities and the nature and the impact of the use of dissolvable tobacco products on the public health, including such use on children.[39] TPSAC issued its findings and recommendations regarding the public health impact of menthol in July 2011.[40]

TPSAC concluded that. "Removal of menthol cigarettes from the marketplace would benefit public health in the United States." However, TPSAC did not recommend a specific mechanism, timeline, or regulatory action that FDA might pursue to address this conclusion.

Concurrently, a multi-step review process was undertaken by FDA to assess the science related to menthol. In developing its evaluation, FDA took the following steps:

- Weighed the collective body of evidence for the impact of menthol cigarette use on public health;
- Evaluated peer-reviewed literature, industry submissions and materials provided to TPSAC; and
- Performed or commissioned analyses to fill in and inform some gaps in the literature.

FDA then submitted its preliminary independent scientific report to a peer review panel. The agency reviewed the peer review comments and prepared responses to them. FDA has made this preliminary independent scientific review available for public comment in the *Federal Register*. The agency also posted the peer reviewed comments and its response to those comments. Based on the evidence and related findings, FDA will consider what actions, if any, are appropriate.[41]

Including its initial meeting in March 2010, the full TPSAC has met 12 times and there have been two meetings of the Tobacco Products Constituents Subcommittee of TPSAC and 2 meetings of the Menthol Report

Subcommittee.[42] In March 2012, TPSAC submitted its recommendations to FDA on the nature and impact of the use of dissolvable tobacco products.[43]

## *NIH Research Collaborations*

In February 2010, FDA launched its Advancing Regulatory Science Initiative to ensure that advances in science and technology are rapidly translated to inform regulatory efforts. As part of the FDA Initiative, NIH has established an organizational structure for managing and coordinating FDA-supported tobacco research at NIH through funding oppmlunities studies, and the establishment of research centers specialized in tobacco research.

## NIH Grants and Supplements

In order to accelerate the pace of tobacco research relevant to tobacco regulation, FDA is funding several competitive NIH research oppmlunities with award budgets of $100,000 to $2,000,000 for one-or two-year research studies related to a variety of areas including the toxicity and addictiveness of tobacco products, consumer perceptions and behaviors related to tobacco products, and product claims and communications.[44] A grant for extended five-year research applications is also available. As of February 28, 2013, FDA had funded 44 research grants through NIH.[45]

## Population Assessment of Tobacco and Health Study

A large scale and critically important research collaboration with NIH is the Population Assessment of Tobacco and Health (PATH) Study. PATH is a national longitudinal cohort study of 59,000 people ages 12 and older in the United States who are tobacco users or at risk for tobacco product use. The study will evaluate initiation and use patterns including use of new products, dual use (using more than one tobacco product), poly use (using more than two tobacco products), and switching between tobacco products; study patterns of tobacco product cessation and relapse; evaluate the effects of regulatory changes on risk perceptions and other tobacco-related attitudes; and assess differences in attitudes and behaviors, and key health outcomes among racial/ethnic, gender, and age subgroups. By measuring and accurately reporting on the social, behavioral, and health effects associated with tobacco product use in the United States, the PATH study will build on an empirical evidence base to inform the development and assessment of tobacco product regulatory activities by FDA.

**Tobacco Research Center Initiatives**

In August 2012, FDA and NIH announced funding to establish Tobacco Centers of Regulatory Science (TCORS). The TCORS program will lead to the creation of a broad coordinated national scientific base of tobacco regulatory research. FDA anticipates funding 14 meritorious TCORS applications in September 2013. Each center is expected to focus thematically on areas in which there are significant gaps in knowledge and other critical areas that will contribute to the science base FDA will use to develop meaningful product regulation. TCORS are expected to fill an urgent need for investigators who have the quality and breadth of training necessary to conduct cutting-edge research related to the regulation of tobacco products and play leadership roles in training new researchers in the field.

Another example of a collaborative research effort with NIH is the FDA-funded center to study nicotine addiction. The overarching goal of this center, established through the National Institute on Drug Abuse (NIDA), is to examine how marked reduction in the nicotine content of cigarettes may impact the use and adverse health effects of such products in current users.

**Other Collaborative Research Activities**

FDA has developed a partnership with the Centers for Disease Control and Prevention (CDC) focused on tobacco research. There are currently projects which use laboratory-based approaches to expanding our knowledge of how best to regulate tobacco products. These include analyses of tobacco products and mainstream smoke, method development for biomarkers, exposure assessments under actual use conditions, and further method development for HPHCs.

In order to provide critical data on the impact of tobacco regulation on populations, FDA has provided funding to expand the scope and increase the frequency of data collection for the National Adult Tobacco Survey (NATS) and National Youth Tobacco Survey (NYTS), both conducted by CDC. NATS is a large, nationally representative cross-sectional, random-digit dialed telephone survey of adults 18 years of age and older. NATS data includes tobacco use prevalence, including novel tobacco products, susceptibility among young adults, as well as perceptions regarding tobacco use, exposure to marketing and promotions, and intentions to quit using tobacco. NYTS is a large, annual, nationally representative survey of middle and high school students that focuses exclusively on tobacco. Data from this survey will allow FDA to monitor awareness of, susceptibility to and experimentation with and use of a wide range of tobacco products. The survey will examine addiction, quitting behaviors, minors' access to tobacco, exposure to tobacco product marketing and promotions, and awareness of health warnings.

FDA is also working with other partners to build scientific knowledge to inform tobacco product regulation. With Sandia National Laboratories, FDA scientists are developing a modeling framework for FDA to use in understanding the impact of certain potential policy and marketing authorization decisions on population health.

FDA's National Center for Toxicological Research (NCTR) and CTP are collaborating on research projects related to tobacco product toxicology, biomarkers of harm, and measures of addictiveness. In addition, CTP is working with NCTR to develop a knowledge base and data mining approach for tobacco constituents that can be used to analyze industry documents on product ingredient and constituent data collected under sections 904(a)(4) and 904(b) of the FD&C Act.

## Scientific publications and communications

FDA scientists have been actively disseminating the results of their research endeavors through manuscripts submitted for publication in scientific journals, as well as submitting abstracts and speaking at major national and international scientific conferences. As of February 28, 2013, CTP scientists had submitted over 70 manuscripts and abstracts and given over 40 presentations at scientific meetings. Topics included:

- Risk perception of dissolvable tobacco products in adults and youth;
- Assessing consumer understanding and risk perception of HPHCs;
- Developing and incorporating tobacco-related questions into the National Health Interview Survey;
- Exploring how little cigars are actually smoked;
- Evaluating tobacco use and cardiovascular diseases;
- Assessing tobacco product incidence in poison control data;
- Developing graphic health warnings;
- Perceptions and behaviors related to cigars, little cigars, cigarillos, water pipes and e-cigarettes;
- Consumer perceptions of risk of tobacco products and studies of modified risk claims; and
- Abuse potential of non-nicotine tobacco smoke components.

FDA has also been proactive in organizing workshops to exchange information with interested stakeholders on important scientific topics related to modified risk tobacco products, FDA's tobacco products research program, and tobacco product analysis.[46]

**FDA Tobacco Regulatory Science Fellowships**

FDA, in collaboration with the Institute of Medicine (IOM) of the National Academies, has launched a new tobacco regulatory science fellowship program designed for mid-career professionals to gain experience and expertise to further define and develop the field of regulatory science as it relates to the regulation of tobacco products and FDA's new authorities under the Tobacco Control Act. The fellowship program provides participants with opportunities to actively participate in the development of science-based public health strategies, serve as the lead for defined projects, meet with policy leaders and develop new competencies, including new knowledge, skills and experience related to tobacco products and their use. The fellowship is a 12-month multidisciplinary residential program based directly out of CTP's offices. The center currently has three fellows and plans to expand the program.

## 6. Restrict Marketing and Distribution to Protect Public Health

Restrictions on marketing and distribution of regulated tobacco products are critical tools authorized by the Tobacco Control Act to protect the public health in a variety of ways, including by preventing youth from purchasing tobacco products.

### *Final Rule on Cigarettes and Smokeless Tobacco*

The Tobacco Control Act required the FDA to publish, in the *Federal Register,* a final rule on cigarettes and smokeless tobacco identical in its provisions, with certain exceptions, to part 897 of the rule published in the *Federal Register* on August 28, 1996.[47] This rule, "Regulations Restricting the Sale and Distribution of Cigarettes and Smokeless Tobacco to Protect Children and Adolescents," published in March 2010, prohibits the sale of cigarettes or smokeless tobacco to people younger than 18 years of age. Among other things, it also bans the sale of cigarette packages with fewer than 20 cigarettes; requires face-to-face sales of cigarettes and smokeless tobacco, with certain exemptions for vending machines and self-service displays in adult-only facilities; and prohibits free samples of cigarettes. Further, the rule limits the distribution of free samples of smokeless tobacco products to circumstances where specific conditions are met, bars tobacco brand name sponsorship of any athletic, musical, or other social or cultural event, or any team or entry in those events, and proscribes the sale or distribution of items such as hats and t-shirts with cigarette and smokeless tobacco brands or logos.[48]

Additionally, FDA has issued an advanced notice of proposed rulemaking to obtain information related to the outdoor advertising of cigarettes and smokeless tobacco. [49]

### Remote sales

In order to prevent sales to minors, the FD&C Act also required FDA to issue regulations regarding the non-face-to-face sale and distribution of regulated tobacco products between retailers and consumers as well as the promotion, and marketing of such products.[50] Following passage of the Tobacco Control Act, the Prevent All Cigarette Trafficking (PACT) Act of 2009 was enacted and went into effect.[51] Among other things, this law requires Internet and other remote sellers of cigarettes, smokeless tobacco, and roll-your-own tobacco to verify the age of customers prior to sales through commercially-available databases and to use a delivery method that requires verification of the age and identification of the person accepting the tobacco products.[52]

Prior to issuing a regulation as required by Section 906(d)(4)(A)(i) of the FD&C Act, FDA determined that additional information was needed concerning non-face-to-face sales and distribution practices in light of the PACT Act. In September 2011, the FDA published an advanced notice of proposed rulemaking in the *Federal Register* to request comments, data, research, or other information related to non-face-to-face sale and distribution of tobacco products; the advertising, promotion, and marketing of such products; and the advertising of tobacco products via the Internet, email, direct mail, telephone, smart phones, and other communication technologies that can be directed to specific recipients.[53] Currently, FDA is evaluating responses and data to determine the next steps.

### Enforcement Action Plan on Advertising to Youth and Regulation of Free Tobacco Samples

As required by section 1 05(a) of the Tobacco Control Act, FDA issued its "Enforcement Action Plan for Promotion and Advertising Restrictions," in October 2010.[54] This Enforcement Action Plan (EAP) describes how FDA plans to enforce restrictions on the promotion and advertising of menthol and other cigarettes, including efforts directed toward youth and particularly toward youth in minority communities. The various components of the EAP are intended to promptly identify and address tobacco products that potentially violate the FD&C Act and illegal sales and distribution of regulated tobacco products. Under the EAP, FDA will also monitor adveliising activities by regulated industry. Additionally, as required by section 102(a)(2)(D)(4) of the Tobacco Control Act, FDA submitted a report to Congress in December 2010 that identified activities addressing the distribution of free samples of regulated tobacco products.

FDA continues to implement and develop its enforcement activities required under the Tobacco Control Act related to both the EAP and distribution of free samples of regulated tobacco products. FDA monitors the progress and effectiveness of these programs to ensure that overall goals and objectives are met and to determine if other restrictions or tools are needed. FDA also educates regulated industry to promote voluntary compliance and collaborates with governmental agencies, consumers, regulated industry, and other stakeholders.

## 7. Ensure Industry's Compliance with FDA Regulations

### *Compliance Training and Assistance*

Rigorous compliance training and education are key components of a successful enforcement program to ensure that the overall goals and objectives of the Tobacco Control Act are achieved. In order to work with regulated tobacco retailers, manufacturers, distributors, wholesalers, importers, as well as other federal, state, local, and tribal authorities to achieve enforcement goals, FDA has established a comprehensive program for training and assistance about the requirements of the Tobacco Control Act.

FDA initially focused its compliance training efforts on tobacco retailers in order to facilitate retailer compliance with the final rule on cigarettes and smokeless tobacco, which became effective in June 2010. Between July and September 2010 CTP staff traveled to five locations across the country to provide information to retailers and small tobacco product manufacturers about the requirements of the rule. These five sessions were panel discussions that provided a forum for questions and answers. Participants could attend in person, call into the sessions, or participate using the Internet.

FDA compliance training efforts later evolved into interactive webinars covering topics pertinent to the broader FDA-regulated tobacco industry. As of February 28, 2013, FDA had conducted 23 of these interactive webinars.

Eleven of these webinars focused on topics pertinent to tobacco retailers, while ten were more relevant to tobacco manufacturers. Two covered topics of interest to both sectors of regulated industry.[55]

As required by Section 901 (f) of the FD&C Act, FDA established the Office of Small Business Assistance (OSBA) within CTP to assist small tobacco product manufacturers and retailers in complying with the Tobacco Control Act. The office has a dedicated webpage, e-mail address, and staff to assist small businesses with their questions, comments, and concerns. OSBA had received approximately 1,900 inquiries through February 28, 2013. All inquiries received are tracked to ensure timely and appropriate responses. In addition, these questions can become topics for future compliance training webinars or other outreach efforts.

FDA has also contracted with an American Indian-owned company to further its efforts to collaborate with American Indian tribes and gain in sight on the best approaches to disseminate information about the Tobacco Control Act to Indian tribes and to tobacco business located on tribal lands. This contractor will also help FDA notify these communities of the availability of formal collaborations for Tribal Nations and organizations to assist FDA in its compliance and enforcement activities as envisioned in the Tobacco Control Act.

For some compliance and enforcement matters, FDA works with other divisions within HHS, U.S. Customs and Border Protection (CBP), the Alcohol and Tobacco Tax and Trade Bureau (TTB), the Bureau of Alcohol, Tobacco, Firearms, and Explosives (ATF), the Federal Trade Commission (FTC), the Department of Justice (DOJ), the National Association of Attorneys General, and other entities, as needed, to ensure compliance and enforcement efforts are coordinated.

In addition, FDA conducts outreach to non-federal government stakeholders involved in tobacco control efforts through a variety of mechanisms including attending conferences and conducting meetings by telephone and videoconference. This outreach has provided opportunities to assist these entities with incorporating FDA's tobacco retail inspection program into their existing tobacco control framework.

### *Retailer Compliance*

Vigorous enforcement of tobacco laws and regulations is calTied out through tobacco retail compliance check inspections. The resulting compliance and enforcement actions can help protect the health ofAmelica's youth and the public health generally by reducing youth access to regulated tobacco products. It also helps to prevent the marketing and advertising of regulated tobacco products to children and adolescents.

Section 702(B) of the FD&C Act instructs FDA to contract, where feasible, with the states, to can-y out inspections of retailers in connection with the enforcement of the Tobacco Control Act. This framework required FDA to implement a tobacco retail compliance and enforcement program that is unique within FDA.

On March 23, 2010, FDA published its initial "Request for Proposals (RFP) to States and U.S. Territories" to launch a program to assist FDA with inspections of retail establishments and other enforcement activities applicable to FDA-regulated tobacco retailers. Since then, FDA has issued additional solicitations for similar inspection activities. FDA will seek alternatives, such as conducting inspections using FDA personnel, in the jurisdictions where contracts are not feasible.

FDA awarded contracts to 15 states in FY 2010 and 37 states and the District of Columbia in FY 2011. FDA awarded contracts to six additional states and territories in FY 2012 and has awarded one additional contract in FY 2013 for a total of 45 contracts. The agency expects to award contracts to additional jurisdictions in FY 2013. FDA will work to continue these contracts and fin1her expand the program. A complete listing of these contracts is available in Appendix C.

These compliance check inspections determine a retailer's compliance with applicable provisions in the Tobacco Control Act and its implementing regulations that include, but are not limited to, the final Rule "Regulations Restricting the Sale and Distribution of Cigarettes and Smokeless Tobacco to Protect Children and Adolescents."

The retail inspection program provides a framework for a nationwide FDA enforcement strategy through the credentialing of more than 900 state and territorial officials and a comprehensive training program for these FDA-commissioned inspectors and program coordinators. These inspectors conduct two types of compliance check inspections for FDA. The first type of compliance check inspection is generally an undercover purchase by an FDA-commissioned inspector and minor to determine whether retailers are checking identification and if they are selling regulated tobacco products to minors. The second type of compliance check inspection involves only FDA-commissioned inspectors and generally determines compliance with other retail provisions in effect, such as the restrictions on impersonal modes of sales (i.e., vending machines and self-service displays), the ban on cigarettes with certain characterizing flavors, and the ban on the sale of packages containing fewer than 20 cigarettes.

FDA had to develop the inspection forms, determine the most appropriate means for collecting the inspection data (most inspectors use mobile devices and have a backup paper system), develop an IT system to support the inspection data from dozens of state and territorial agencies across the country, and develop means to incorporate this inspection data into FDA's existing IT systems.

FDA continues to update and enhance its mobile device inspection tool using customized software known as the Tobacco Inspection Management Systems Mobile Application. The tool helps reduce the amount of equipment inspectors need, reduce or eliminate the need to mail, fax, or scan paper forms to and from field inspectors, and reduces data entry, thereby decreasing the time for conducting and reviewing inspections and gathering evidence.

Each year FDA has expanded its retail inspection program and continues to enhance this program by streamlining processes; updating training; and upgrading IT systems, applications and hardware. As additional provisions applicable to retailers are implemented, they will be included in these contracts for compliance check inspections.

### Advisory and Enforcement Authorities

When potential violations are observed during a compliance check inspection of a tobacco retailer, FDA reviews the evidence and detemlines what action should be taken. FDA may utilize several administrative and enforcement tools provided for in the Tobacco Control Act and the FD&C Act, including: warning letters, civil money penalties (CMP), no-tobacco-sale orders, seizures, injunctions, and/or criminal prosecutions. Many of these tools are also used when violations by other FDA-regulated entities such as manufacturers, distributers, importers, and online retailers are found by FDA.

A warning letter is the agency's principal means of notifying regulated industry of a violation and is used to achieve prompt voluntary compliance with the law. FDA generally issues warning letters to tobacco retailers the first time violations are observed during a compliance check inspection.

A CMP complaint is used to initiate an administrative legal action against a retailer that can result in the imposition of a fine. FDA generally issues CMP complaints to tobacco retailers when violations are observed during compliance check inspections after inspections that resulted in a warning letter. FDA follows the penalty schedule outlined in Section 103(c) and (q) of the Tobacco Control Act and included in Appendix D of this report.

The results of all compliance check inspections, including those inspections with no observed violations, are available on the FDA website in a searchable database with links to all issued warning letters and CMP complaints.

Measurable accomplishments in the retail inspection program since the date of enactment through February 28 include:

- Awarding more than $62 million in contracts to 45 states and territories to assist CTP in enforcing tobacco marketing, sale, and distribution laws and regulations at retail locations;
- Conducting more than 147,000 compliance check inspections of regulated tobacco retailers utilizing state and territorial contractors;
- Issuing over 7,740 warning letters to retail establishments where violations were found during compliance check inspections;
- Issuing over 520 CMP administrative actions to retail establishments where subsequent violations were found during follow -up compliance check inspections; and
- Developing a searchable database of retail compliance check inspection results.

### *Promotion, Advertising and Labeling Compliance*

Active and effective enforcement of tobacco Jaws and regulations governing the promotion, advertising, and labeling of tobacco products can help to protect the public health by preventing the sale and distribution of misbranded and adulterated tobacco products, including those with marketing and advertising materials that violate the requirements of the Tobacco Control Act.

FDA enforces the Tobacco Control Act and its regulations for the promotion, advertising and labeling of regulated tobacco products including: review and evaluation of regulatory submissions that include tobacco product labeling, representative advertising, and consumer infomlation materials; routine monitoring and surveillance of websites and publications that sell, distribute, promote, or adveliise regulated tobacco products; and surveillance of event promotion and sponsorship by tobacco manufacturers, distributors, or retailers.

In establishing its compliance and enforcement progranl for warning statements on smokeless tobacco product labeling and advertising, FDA consulted with DOJ as well as FTC, from which responsibilities under the Comprehensive Smokeless Tobacco Health Education Act of 1986 (Smokeless

Tobacco Act),[56] as amended by section 204 of the Tobacco Control Act, were transitioned to FDA.

FDA has issued a number of letters to manufacturers requesting information regarding their marketing and advertising practices to ensure compliance with applicable provisions under laws enforced by FDA. For example, FDA has requested information on events that include the distribution of free samples of smokeless tobacco products, internet marketing activities, and other relevant information to determine compliance.

Since the date of enactment through February 28, 2013, FDA's promotion, advertising, and labeling compliance and enforcement program has accomplished the following:

- Identifying more than 2,000 websites where regulated tobacco products might be sold, distributed or advertised and determining that over 160 of these web sites were in violation of the Tobacco Control Act.
- Conducting surveillance of approximately 6,600 unique publications, identifying and evaluating approximately 2,500 advertisements of regulated tobacco products in the U.S. market to determine compliance with advertising and promotion requirements;
- Issuing over 95 warning letters as a result of CTP's internet and publication surveillance and review and evaluation of consumer/ public complaints (some warning letters covered multiple websites);
- Issuing two warning letters as a result of event promotion and sponsorship surveillance, resulting in compliance in both instances;
- Reviewing approximately 160 product listing submissions with labeling, advertising, and consumer information materials;
- Reviewing 35 smokeless tobacco warning plans and 10 smokeless tobacco warning plan supplements in accordance with the Smokeless Tobacco Act, as amended by Section 204 of the Tobacco Control Act;
- Reviewing 16 notices of the use of other media, which included 25 web sites, for advertising and promotion of tobacco products; and
- Issuing nine information requests to tobacco product manufacturers seeking additional information on promotional activities and sponsorship, and nine requests to manufacturers seeking access to their direct-mailer materials and product websites, with all requests for direct-mailer materials and active websites granted.

## *Manufacturer Compliance and Enforcement Activities*

As directed in Section 905(g) of the FD&C Act, FDA conducts biennial inspections of registered tobacco product establishments that manufacture regulated tobacco products in the U.S. market. These inspections are designed to determine compliance with requirements of the FD&C Act. These include registration, product and ingredient listing, packaging, labeling, and advertising requirements, and marketing authorization for new or modified risk tobacco products.

To ensure this compliance and enforcement program is effectively implemented, FDA provides its tobacco investigators with comprehensive and continued training on the inspection requirements. These requirements differ in many ways from inspections requirements for products traditionally regulated by FDA.

Further, FDA collaborates with CBP on import operations for tobacco products. FDA conducts field exams and maintains import bulletins and alerts that identify tobacco products in violation of the FD&C Act, which may be detained. Imported tobacco products must conform to the same regulatory requirements as domestic tobacco products. Examples of products that may be detained include those that are labeled or advertised using the descriptors "light," "mild," or "low," without an FDA order, and cigarettes or their component parts that are labeled as having certain characterizing flavors.

FDA has expanded the capacity of agency laboratories to analyze tobacco products. These laboratories conduct analysis of tobacco samples to develop methods, validate methods, establish products standards and baselines, and identify ingredients to support future FDA enforcement actions. FDA plans to continue expanding the capabilities of these laboratories.

In the area of manufacturing compliance and enforcement FDA's measurable accomplishments through February 28, 2013, include:

- Conducting 73 inspections of registered tobacco product facilities;
- Conducting 11 investigations that included sponsorship events and distribution of free sample events; and
- Reviewing over 50,000 lines of imported tobacco products, completing over 1,100 field exams and more than 1,600 label exams, and refusing 59 entries, in collaboration with CBP. FDA issued two import bulletins and subsequent import alerts that directed many of these reviews and exams.

*Complaint Submissions*

FDA established a complaint submission system with a website and hotline for the public and other stakeholders to report possible violations of the Tobacco Control Act. FDA recently started providing another option for reporting potential violations with its new Potential Tobacco Product Violations Reporting form.[57] The information provided is reviewed by FDA to determine what follow-up action, if any, is appropriate. FDA does not initiate enforcement actions solely on the basis of complaints from the public.

FDA is developing a database for these complaints. Since the system was launched in March 2010 through the end of 2012, FDA received and detem1ined appropriate action for approximately 500 complaints.


## 8. Educate the Public

*Public Education Campaigns*

The Tobacco Control Act amends the FD&C Act by giving FDA the authority to regulate tobacco products, including educating the public about the dangers of regulated tobacco product use. To advance efforts to protect the public from the harmful effects of tobacco use, FDA is developing integrated, far-reaching, and evidence-based public education campaigns related to FDA's regulatory activities. These campaigns are focused on preventing tobacco initiation, and promoting tobacco use cessation, particularly among the nation's youth and young adults.

As part of this comprehensive strategy for public education, FDA announced the award of nine contracts in calendar year 2012, dedicating up to $600 million over five years to conduct sustained, multi-media campaigns that will enable FDA to educate the public, and vulnerable youth populations in particular, about the harms and risks of regulated tobacco products in order to help prevent initiation and encourage cessation. Specifically, these campaigns will equip the public with important facts about:

- The health risks of regulated tobacco products;
- The addictiveness of regulated tobacco products;
- HPHCs in regulated tobacco products; and
- The public health basis for marketing restrictions on regulated tobacco products, such as those on using the descriptors "light," "mild,"' or "low."

In awarding these contracts, FDA developed two expert campaign contractor pools: one open to competition from all potential contractors designed to focus on general market campaigns, and one limited to small business contractors designed to focus on vulnerable and underserved populations. A complete listing of contract awardees is included in Appendix E.

As early as December 2013, FDA plans to launch the first of its multiple, integrated public health campaigns focused on preventing tobacco initiation and promoting tobacco use cessation among the nation's youth and young adults by educating them on the dangers of regulated tobacco products. The campaigns will include a mix of traditional television and print ads, local events, and digital strategies. The campaigns will focus on the following distinct, targeted audiences: at-risk youth ages 12-15 that are African American; Hispanic; Asian/Pacific Islander; reside in rural communities; or identify as LGBTQ. Another set of campaigns will target general market youth ages 12-17 who have not yet initiated tobacco use and those who are intermittent users. FDA is also committed to reaching additional at-risk populations with high tobacco prevalence including Native American and Alaskan Native audiences.

In addition, FDA is overseeing a variety of research and analytic activities to strengthen and inform public education initiatives and efforts. This includes awarding a five-year, $60 million contract to conduct rigorous outcome evaluations on the effectiveness of individual FDA tobacco-related public education campaigns, overall messaging, and related communications activities.

This combination of establishing and evaluating evidence-based national campaigns will enable FDA to implement effective models for educating the public about the risks and dangers of regulated products. These efforts will also complement public education initiatives by partner agencies on tobacco related issues.

### *Regulatory Actions for Prescribed Health Warnings*

FDA also seeks to inform the public about the negative health consequences of tobacco product use with the product warning labels required under Title II of the Tobacco Control Act.

### Graphic Health Warnings

The Federal Cigarette Labeling and Advertising Act (FCLAA),[58] as amended by Section 201 of the Tobacco Control Act, contains requirements for health warnings and graphic label statements depicting the negative health consequences of smoking that must appear on cigarette product packages and advertisements. FCLAA, as amended by Section 201 of the Tobacco Control Act, also requires the submission of plans for the rotation and distribution of labeling statements on cigarette product packages and advertisements to FDA for review and approval, rather than to the FTC.

On June 11, 2011, FDA published the final rule entitled "Required Warnings for Cigarette Packages and Advertisements." The rule would require warnings, which consist of a textual warning statement, a corresponding color graphic image depicting the negative health consequences of smoking, and a toll-free smoking cessation assistance resource phone number (together known as a "required warning"), to appear on all cigarette packages and advertisements. The rule would require the warnings to be either indelibly printed or pem1anently affixed, in the same orientation as the other information on the packages, and clearly visible on the top 50 percent of the front and back panels of cigarette packages and the top 20 percent of the area of cigarette advertisement.

Prior to selecting the required warnings, FDA conducted an Internet-based consumer research study with over 18,000 participants that examined 36 proposed graphic health warnings. FDA evaluated the relative effectiveness of each graphic health warning for conveying information about various health risks of smoking, encouraging cessation, and discouraging smoking initiation. The results of the study, along with relevant scientific literature, indicated that the warnings selected by FDA would effectively communicate the negative health consequences of smoking to a wide range of populations including smokers and nonsmokers. Other research has shown that graphic health warnings are associated with smokers' increased motivation to quit smoking and indicates that, in general, graphic health warnings are more effective if they are combined with cessation-related information such as a toll-free smoking cessation assistance line.

In August 2012, the United States Court of Appeals for the D.C. Circuit upheld the D.C. district court' s decision vacating the rule.[59] A two-judge majority held that the rule violated the First Amendment because the government did not provide sufficient evidence that the rule directly advances a government interest. As a consequence, FDA's 2011 graphic health warning rule for cigarettes will not be implemented, and FDA will undertake research to support a new rulemaking consistent with the Tobacco Control Act. Current FTC requirements for health warnings on cigarettes remain in effect.

**Smokeless Tobacco Health Warnings**

The Smokeless Tobacco Act, as amended by Section 204 of the Tobacco Control Act, requires health warning statements that must appear on smokeless tobacco product packages and advertisements, and requires the submission of warning plans for smokeless tobacco product packages and advertisements to FDA for review and approval, rather than to the FTC. As amended, Section 3(b)(3) of the Smokeless Tobacco Act requires the equal distribution and display of warning statements on packaging, and the quarterly rotation of warning statements in advertising, for each brand of smokeless tobacco product, "in accordance with a plan submitted by the tobacco product manufacturer, importer, distributor, or retailer" and approved by FDA.

In September 2011, FDA published a draft guidance discussing, among other things, the statutory requirement to submit warning plans, who submits a warning plan, the scope of a warning plan, and what information should be submitted to FDA.[60]

*Public Outreach*

FDA is committed to building a deep knowledge of tobacco product manufacturing, marketing and dist1ibution as well as establishing and maintaining meaningful and appropriate relationships with industry. This includes manufacturers, distributors and wholesalers, retailers and trade associations. These relationships increase FDA's understanding of the tobacco industry and its members while building the industry's understanding of the FDA and regulatory process.

FDA is also committed to establishing and maintaining meaningful and appropriate relationships with public health groups and other organizations involved in tobacco control and public health and to fostering collaboration with other government agencies with responsibilities relative to tobacco products or related public health issues. This facilitates the dissemination of information on tobacco-related priorities and activities to public health stakeholders including state, tribal, territorial, and local tobacco control programs. Other federal government partners include CDC, NIH, TTB, ATF, and the Substance Abuse and Mental Health Services Administration (SAMHSA).

CTP maintains regular contact with a broad array of organizations to ensure their full understanding of the goals and objectives of the Tobacco Control Act and awareness of opportunities to actively participate in the regulatory process. This consistent outreach conveys FDA's desire and commitment to stay engaged with communities interested in FDA's regulation of tobacco products. It creates opportunities to communicate about ways to amplify FDA's education campaigns and serves to strengthen and advance the development and implementation of FDA's regulatory actions, policies and initiatives.

Outreach efforts to the industry and public health communities include a listening session program. These sessions provide opportunities for interested parties to share their perspectives on topics including SE, Roll-Your-Own Tobacco Mislabeled as Pipe Tobacco, Electronic Cigarette Regulation, Cigar Regulation, Smoking Cessation via Nicotine Inhaler, Illicit Trade of Tobacco Products, Tobacco Related Health Disparities, and Tobacco Evaluation, Surveillance, and Research.

As of February 28, CTP had held over 30 listening sessions with a broad array of parties including:

- *21st Century Smoke*
- *Altria*
- *American Cancer Society*
- *American Lung Association*
- *American Wholesale Marketers Association (AWMA)*
- *Aradigm Corporation*
- *Campaign for Tobacco Free Kids*
- *Cigar Association of America*
- *Cigars International*
- *Chronic Obstructive Pulmonary Disease (COPD) Foundation*
- *Council of Independent Tobacco Manufacturers of America*
- *National Heart Forum*
- *Drew Estate Cigars*
- *Electronic Cigarette Industry Group*
- *FIN E-Cigarettes*
- *General Cigar*
- *International Premium Cigar and Pipe Retailers*
- *Legacy*
- *Liggett Vector Brands*
- *Lorillard*
- *MayaTech*
- *National Association of Convenience Stores (NACS)*
- *National Networks for Tobacco-Related Health Disparities*
- *North American Quitline Consortium*

- *PARRS Brands*
- *Republic Tobacco*
- *Jet Cigs E-Cigarettes*
- *Pipe Tobacco Council*
- *Roswell Park Cancer Institute*
- *Small Manufacturers Association for the Reasonable Treatment of 'Tobacco*
- *Smoke Free Alternative Trade Association*
- *Snoke-E-Cigarette Company*
- *Survos*
- *Swedish Match*
- *The Institute for Global Tobacco Control*
- *Tobacco Control Legal Consortium*
- *University of Medicine and Dentistly* of New *Jersey Center for Tobacco Control Evaluation, Surveillance and Research*
- *University of North Carolina Gillings* School of *Public Health*

In addition to listening sessions, FDA participates in many tobacco industry and public health events. Some of the tobacco industry events have included: the Tobacco Merchants Association Annual Meeting and Conference, the National Association of Tobacco Outlets Annual Show and NACS Show. Some of the public health related events have included: the National Conference on Tobacco or Health, the Annual Conference of the Association of State and Territorial Health Officials, National Association of Local Boards of Health Annual Meeting, the National Association of County and City Health Officials Annual Conference, the Annual Conference of the American Public Health Association, and the Annual Conference of the Society for Research on Nicotine and Tobacco.

Often these exchanges serve as an opportunity to give notice of open dockets available for comment and reminders of the comment periods' closing dates. FDA has received questions as a result of this outreach and provided timely responses.

### *International Engagement*

In order to advance its regulatory mission to reduce tobacco use and banns in the United States, FDA engages international stakeholders and industry organizations in an effort to educate others about FDA's authorities and obtain information from the global tobacco control community, including regulators in other countries. These opportunities enable FDA to explain its tobacco control authorities to interested parties and allow FDA to gather, analyze and develop international data, and research that can inform the development of effective policy, guidance, and regulations aimed at protecting Americans from tobacco-related death and disease.

For example, in September 2010 FDA hosted an "Embassy Briefing" to introduce FDA's new tobacco program to Washington D.C.'s diplomatic community. In November 2011, FDA also co-sponsored the first *International Tobacco Regulators Conference* with the World Health Organization (WHO), which brought together 65 foreign government officials from 25 countries to discuss tobacco control issues of common interest. In November 2012, FDA participated as an observer in the 5th Session of the Conference of the Parties for the Framework Convention on Tobacco Control. In addition, FDA is an active member of the WHO Tobacco Laboratory Network, an effort dedicated to advancing the development of laboratory methods, standards, expertise, and capacity for tobacco products testing and research; the International Standards Organization's Technical Advisory Group for Tobacco and Tobacco Products (TC 126); and the Cooperation Centre for Scientific Research Relative to Tobacco. FDA will continue to identify opportunities for international engagement on tobacco control issues to support its regulatory mission.

### Ombudsman

An important part of FDA's public outreach is conducted by the CTP Ombudsman. The role of the Ombudsman is to: (1) advise the Center Director on ways to assure that CTP' s procedures, policies, and decisions are of the highest quality and are fair and equitable; (2) to examine complaints from stakeholders; and (3) to facilitate the resolution of disputes with impartiality, neutrality, and fairness. The Ombudsman is an independent source for stakeholders to address complaints and inquiries, seek the resolution of disputes of a scientific, regulatory, or procedural nature, and discuss appeal and dispute resolution options. The Ombudsman engages in outreach to stakeholders by attending, mld presenting and networking at external meetings and conferences, as well as stakeholder forums hosted by CTP.

# IV. CHALLENGES AND OPPORTUNITIES

With the Tobacco Control Act in place, the United States has reached a new frontier in combating tobacco use and FDA's CTP is at the forefront of this effort.

Some of the challenges FDA has faced in these early years are the growing pains inherent in building a regulatory body from the ground up. FDA has worked through the logistical challenges of creating infrastructure and an organizational structure, recruiting and hiring qualified staff with applicable experience in a short time frame, and developing the processes, procedures and dedicated infomlation technology resources to carry out regulatory functions.

There are challenges intrinsic to the regulation of tobacco products, which are markedly different from other products traditionally regulated by FDA. In this early stage, for example, FDA has had to create and validate entirely new scientific testing procedures for the measurement of HPHCs in tobacco products and tobacco smoke and develop metrics for the evaluation of product applications, including the 4,253 substantial equivalence applications now under review. With limited institutional experience to rely upon, FDA also had to establish and implement a tobacco retail compliance program that is unique even within FDA. Moreover, with tobacco product regulation, FDA has had the challenge of regulating an industry that is entirely new to federal product regulation and often unfamiliar with what is expected in the FDA regulatory process.

In addition, FDA had been unable to implement certain provisions in the Tobacco Control Act that were challenged in the courts, such as the requirement that all cigarette packages bear one of nine new textual warnings and include color graphics depicting the negative health consequences of smoking. The government decided not to seek further review of the D.C. Circuit decision in R.J. Reynolds Tobacco Co. v. FDA, Nos. 11-5332; 12-5063 (D.C. Cir.), formerly CA No. 111482 (D.D.C.), invalidating FDA's rule regarding graphic health warning labels for cigarettes. The court of appeals remanded the matter to the agency, and FDA will undertake research to support a new rulemaking consistent with the Tobacco Control Act.

Moving forward, FDA will be challenged to sustain the momentum needed to achieve its goals for reducing the harms and risks associated with tobacco product use, given the common misperception that decades of tobacco control research, program and policy efforts have solved this problem. The reality is that despite decades of scientific research and public health efforts, tobacco use continues to be the leading cause of preventable death and disease in the United States. Cigarette smoking results in 5.1 million years of potential life lost in the United States annually and the total economic burden of cigarette smoking is estimated to be $193 billion in annual health care and productivity costs.[61]

Perhaps the greatest opportunity FDA has to overcome this pressing public health problem is to dramatically decrease the access and appeal of tobacco products to youth. According to the Surgeon General's 2012 report, "Tobacco Use: A Preventable Epidemic," 90 percent of smokers start smoking by age 18 and 99 percent start by age 26. Although the report notes years of steady progress, declines in the use of tobacco by youth and young adults have slowed for cigarette smoking and stalled for smokeless tobacco use. FDA aims to use the tools at its disposal to continue the decline in tobacco use and to reinvigorate public determination to arrest the epidemic by making the next generation tobacco free.

## V. Conclusion

FDA regulation of tobacco products has opened a bold new chapter in America's fight to decrease the 443,000 preventable deaths caused by tobacco use each year. It is an essential comers tone of the broader efforts led by HHS in partnership with other federal agencies and public health practitioners working in state, territorial, tribal, and local governments. Within HHS, coordination between FDA, NIH, CDC, and SAMHSA has focused on maximizing the impact and efficiency of agency programs focused on tobacco control.

In the nearly four years since the enactment of the Tobacco Control Act, FDA has made substantial progress toward establishing a comprehensive, effective, and sustainable framework for tobacco product regulation aimed at protecting the public from the harms of tobacco products, encouraging cessation among tobacco users, and preventing new users from starting.

These major strides include, among other things:

- Creating the new Center for Tobacco Products;
- Undertaking critical scientific research to inform the evaluation of tobacco products and the development of product standards;
- Promulgating science-based regulations and guidance;
- Enforcing compliance with new tobacco product requirements; and
- Developing effective strategies to educate the public about the characteristics and dangers of regulated tobacco products.

FDA remains committed to advancing these achievements to make tobacco-related death and disease part of America's past, not its future.

# APPENDIX A. REGULATIONS, GUIDANCE DOCUMENTS, AND OTHER REGULATORY DOCUMENTS ISSUED BY FDA RELATED TO THE FAMILY SMOKING PREVENTION AND TOBACCO CONTROL ACT

| Type | Title | Date Issued |
|---|---|---|
| Final Rule | Exemptions From Substantial Equivalence Requirements | 7/5/2011 |
| Final Rule | Required Warnings for Cigarette Packages and Advertisements | 6/22/2011 |
| Final Rule | Amendments to General Regulations of the Food and Drug Administration | 11/30/2010 |
| Final Rule | Regulations Restricting the Sale and Distribution of Cigarettes and Smokeless Tobacco | 3/18/2010 |
| Notice of Proposed Rulemaking (NPRM) | Regulations Restricting the Sale and Distribution of Cigarettes and Smokeless Tobacco to Protect Children and Adolescents (Amends Brand Name Provision (1140.16(a)) | 11/10/2011 |
| Advanced Notice of Proposed Rulemaking (ANPRM) | Non-Face-to-Face Sale and Distribution of Tobacco Products and Advertising, Promotion, and Marketing of Tobacco Products; Extension of Comment Period | 12/6/2011 |
| Advanced Notice of Proposed Rulemaking (ANPRM) | Non-Face-to-Face Sale and Distribution of Tobacco Products and Advertising, Promotion, and Marketing of Tobacco Products | 9/9/2011 |
| Advanced Notice of Proposed Rulemaking (ANPRM) | Outdoor Advertising Provision | 3/19/2010 |
| Guidance | Civil Money Penalties and No-Tobacco-Sale Orders For Tobacco Retailers | 11/2/2012 |
| Guidance | Meetings with Industry and Investigators on the Research and Development of Tobacco Products | 5/24/2012 |

## Appendix A. (Continued)

| Type | Title | Date Issued |
|---|---|---|
| Guidance | Further Amendments to General Regulations of the Food and Drug Administration to Incorporate Tobacco Products | 3/30/2012 |
| Guidance | Required Warnings for Cigarette Packages and Advertisements | 10/24/201 1 |
| Guidance | Enforcement Policy Concerning Certain Regulations Restricting the Sale and Distribution of Cigarettes and Smokeless Tobacco | 5/7/2011 |
| Guidance | "Harmful and Potentially Harmful Constituents" in Tobacco Products as Used in Section 904(e) of the Federal Food, Drug, and Cosmetic Act | 1/31/2011 |
| Guidance | Reports: Demonstrating Substantial Equivalence for Tobacco Products | 1/5/2011 |
| Guidance | Use of "Light," "Mild," "Low," or Similar Descriptors in the Label, Labeling, or Advertising of Tobacco Products | 6/10/2010 |
| Guidance | Tobacco Health Document Submission | 4/20/2010 |
| Guidance | General Questions and Answers on the Ban of Cigarettes that Contain Certain Characte1izing Flavors (Edition 2) | 12/23/2009 |
| Guidance | Time frame for Submission of Tobacco Health Documents | 12/21/2009 |
| Guidance | Listing of Ingredients in Tobacco Products | 12/1/2009 |
| Guidance | Registration and Product Listing for Owners and Operators of Domestic Tobacco Product Establishments | 11/12/2009 |
| Draft Guidance | Civil Money Penalties for Tobacco Retailers-Responses to Frequently Asked Questions | 2/8/2013 |
| Draft Guidance | Modified Risk Tobacco Product Applications | 4/3/2012 |

| Type | Title | Date Issued |
|------|-------|-------------|
| Draft Guidance | Reporting Harmful and Potentially Harmful Constituents in Tobacco Products and Tobacco Smoke Under Section 904(a)(3) of the Federal Food, Drug, and Cosmetic Act | 4/3/2012 |
| Draft Guidance | Applications for Premarket Review of New Tobacco Products | 9/27/2011 |
| Draft Guidance | Demonstrating the Substantial Equivalence of a New Tobacco Product: Responses to Frequently Asked Questions | 9/22/2011 |
| Draft Guidance | Submission of Warming Plans for Cigarettes and Smokeless Tobacco Products | 9/9/2011 |
| Draft Guidance | Establishing that a Tobacco Product was Commercially Marketed in the United States as of February 15, 2007 | 4/22/2011 |
| Draft Guidance | Compliance with Regulations Restricting the Sale and Distribution of Cigarettes and Smokeless Tobacco To Protect Children and Adolescents [Revision to Draft Guidance]* | 3/23/201 1 |
| Draft Guidance | Tobacco Retailer Training Programs | 7/16/2010 |
| Draft Guidance | Preliminary Timetable for the Review of Applications for Modified Risk Tobacco Products under the Federal Food, Drug, and Cosmetic Act | 1/27/2009 |
| Draft Guidance | The Scope of the Prohibition Against Marketing a Tobacco Product in Combination with Another Article or Product Regulated under the Federal Food, Drug, and Cosmetic Act | 9/30/2009 |
| Established List | Harmful and Potentially Harmful Constituents in Tobacco Products and Tobacco Smoke | 4/3/2012 |
| Enforcement Action Plan | Promotion and Advertising Restrictions | 10/31/2011 |

## APPENDIX B. ESTABLISHED LIST OF THE CHEMICALS AND CHEMICAL COMPOUNDS IDENTIFIED BY FDA AS HARMFUL AND POTENTIALLY HARMFUL CONSTITUENTS IN TOBACCO PRODUCTS AND TOBACCO SMOKE

| Constituent | Carcinogen (CA), Respiratory Toxicant (RT), Cardiovascular Toxicant (CT), Reproductive or Developmental Toxicant (RDT), Addictive (AD) |
|---|---|
| Acetaldehyde | CA, RT, AD |
| Acetamide | CA |
| Acetone | RT |
| Acrolein | RT,CT |
| Acrylamide | CA |
| Acrylonitrile | CA, RT |
| Aflatoxin B1 | CA |
| 4-Aminobiphenyl | CA |
| 1-Aminonaphthalene | CA |
| 2-Aminonaphthalene | CA |
| Ammonia | RT |
| Anabasine | AD |
| o-Anisidine | CA |
| Arsenic | CA, CT, ROT |
| A-α-C (2-Amino-9H-pyrido[2,3-b]indole) | CA |
| Benz[a]anthracene | CA, CT |
| Benz[j]aceanthrylene | CA |
| Benzene | CA, CT, R DT |
| Benzo[b]fluoranthene | CA, CT |
| Benzo[k]fluoranthene | CA,CT |
| Benzo[b]furan | CA |
| Benzo[a]pyrene | CA |
| Benzo[c]phenanthrene | CA |
| Beryllium | CA |
| 1,3-Butadiene | CA, RT, RDT |
| Cadmium | CA, RT, RDT |

| Constituent | Carcinogen (CA), Respiratory Toxicant (RT), Cardiovascular Toxicant (CT), Reproductive or Developmental Toxicant (RDT), Addictive (AD) |
|---|---|
| Caffeic acid | CA |
| Carbon monoxide | ROT |
| Catechol | CA |
| Chlorinated dioxins/furans | CA, RDT |
| Chromium | CA, RT, RDT |
| Chrysene | CA, CT |
| Cobalt | CA, CT |
| Coumarin | Banned in food |
| Cresols (o-, m-, and p-cresol) | CA, RT |
| Crotonaldehyde | CA |
| Cyclopenta [c,d]pyrene | CA |
| Dibenz[a,h]anthracene | CA |
| Dibenzo[a,e]pyrene | CA |
| Dibenzo[a,h]pyrene | CA |
| Dibenzo[a,i]pyrene | CA |
| Dibenzo[a,l]pyrene | CA |
| 2,6-Dimethylaniline | CA |
| Ethyl carbamate (urethane) | CA, RDT |
| Ethylbenzene | CA |
| Ethylene oxide | CA, RT, RDT |
| Formaldehyde | CA, RT |
| Furan | CA |
| Glu-P-1 (2-Amino-6-methyldipyrido[1,2-a:3',2'-d] imidazole) | CA |
| Glu-P-2 (2-Aminodipyrido[1,2-a:3',2'-d]imidazole) | CA |
| Hydrazine | CA, RT |
| Hydrogen cyanide | RT, CT |
| Indeno[1,2,3-cd]pyrene | CA |
| IQ (2-Amino-3-methylimidazo[4,5-f]quinoline) | CA |
| Isoprene | CA |
| Lead | CA, CT, RDT |

**Appendix B. (Continued)**

| Constituent | Carcinogen (CA), Respiratory Toxicant (RT), Cardiovascular Toxicant (CT), Reproductive or Developmental Toxicant (RDT), Addictive (AD) |
|---|---|
| MeA-α-C (2-Amino-3-methyl)-9<u>H</u>-pyrido[2,3-<u>b</u>] indole) | CA |
| Mercury | CA, RDT |
| Methyl ethyl ketone | RT |
| 5-Methylchrysene | CA |
| 4-(Methylnitrosamino)-1-(3-pyridyl)1-butanone (NNK) | CA |
| Naphthalene | CA, RT |
| Nickel | CA, RT |
| Nicotine | RDT, AD |
| Nitrobenzene | CA, RT, RDT |
| Nitromethane | CA |
| 2-Nitropropane | CA |
| <u>N</u>-Nitrosodiethanolamine (NDELA) | CA |
| <u>N</u>-Nitrosodiethylamine | CA |
| <u>N</u>-Nitrosodimethylamine (NDMA) | CA |
| <u>N</u>-Nitrosomethylethyl amine | CA |
| <u>N</u>-Nitrosomorpholine (NMOR) | CA |
| <u>N</u>-Nitrosonomicotine (NNN) | CA |
| <u>N</u>-Nitrosopiperidine (NPIP) | CA |
| <u>N</u>-Nitrosopynolidine (NPYR) | CA |
| <u>N</u>-Nitrososarcosine (NSAR) | CA |
| Nornicotine | AD |
| Phenol | RT, CT |
| PhIP (2-Amino-1-methyl-6-Phenylimidazo[4,5-<u>b</u>] pyridine) | CA |
| Polonium-2 1 0 | CA |
| Propionaldehyde | RT, CT |
| Propylene oxide | CA, RT |
| Quinoline | CA |

| Constituent | Carcinogen (CA), Respiratory Toxicant (RT), Cardiovascular Toxicant (CT), Reproductive or Developmental Toxicant (RDT), Addictive (AD) |
|---|---|
| Selenium | RT |
| Styrene | CA |
| o-Toluidine | CA |
| Toluene | RT, RDT |
| Trp-P-1 (3-Amino-1,4-dimethyl-5H-pyrido[4,3-b] indole) | CA |
| Trp-P-2 (1-Methyl-3-amino-5H-pyrido[4,3-b] indole) | CA |
| Uranium-235 | CA, RT |
| Uranium-238 | CA, RT |
| Vinyl acetate | CA, RT |
| Vinyl chloride | CA |

## APPENDIX C. STATE CONTRACTS FOR TOBACCO RETAIL COMPLIANCE CHECK INSPECTIONS AS OF FEBRUARY 28, 2013

| State | Agency | Total Awarded To Date* |
|---|---|---|
| Alabama | Alabama Department of Public Health | $3,546,4 88 |
| Arizona | Arizona Department of Health Services | $1,674,139 |
| Arkansas | Arkansas Tobacco Control Board | $2,126,997 |
| California | California Department of Public Health, Food and Drug Branch | $3,128,796 |
| Colorado | Colorado Department of Public Health and Environment | $2,846,347 |
| Connecticut | Connecticut Department of Mental Health and Addiction Services | $1,248,956 |

**(Continued )**

| State | Agency | Total Awarded To Date* |
|---|---|---|
| Delaware | Delaware Department of Homeland Security, Division of Alcohol and Tobacco Enforcement | $321,982 |
| Georgia | Georgia Department of Revenue, Alcohol and Tobacco Division | $1,285,686 |
| Guam | Guam Department of Mental Health and Substance Abuse | $280,758 |
| Hawaii | Hawaii Department of Health, Alcohol and Drug Abuse Division | $504,629 |
| Idaho | Idaho Department of Health and Welfare | $891,596 |
| Illinois | Illinois Department of Revenue, Illinois Liquor Control Commission | $ 1,954,934 |
| Indiana | Indiana Alcohol and Tobacco Commission, Indiana State Excise Police | $1,614,781 |
| Iowa | Iowa Department of Commerce, Alcoholic Beverages Division | $963,040 |
| Kansas | Kansas Department of Revenue, Alcoholic Beverage Control | $1,462,716 |
| Kentucky | Kentucky Department of Alcoholic Beverage Control | $857,493 |
| Louisiana | Louisiana Office of Alcohol and Tobacco Control | $1,166,014 |
| Maine | Maine Center for Disease Control and Prevention, Division of Chronic Disease | $2,183,970 |
| Maryland | Maryland Department of Health and Mental Hygiene, Alcohol and Drug Abuse Administration | $ 1,886,301 |
| Massachusetts | Massachusetts Department of Public Health, Tobacco Cessation and Prevention Program | $1,706,397 |
| Michigan | Michigan Department of Community Health, Bureau of Substance Abuse and Addiction Services | $1,859,484 |
| Minnesota | Minnesota Department of Health and Human Services, Alcohol and Drug Abuse Division | $1,141,958 |

| State | Agency | Total Awarded To Date* |
|---|---|---|
| Mississippi | Mississippi Attorney General's Office, Alcohol and Tobacco Enforcement Unit | $2,937,165 |
| Missouri | Missouri Department of Mental Health, Division of Alcohol and Drug Abuse | $1,753,465 |
| Montana | Montana Department of Public Health and Human Services | $113,256 |
| New Hampshire | New Hampshire Liquor Commission, Division of Enforcement and Licensing | $399,168 |
| New Jersey | New Jersey Department of Health and Senior Services, Division of Family Health Services, Office of Tobacco Control | $1,642,052 |
| New Mexico | New Mexico Human Services Department, Behavioral Health Services Division | $1,342,642 |
| North Carolina | North Carolina Department of Health and Human Services, Division of Mental Health | $1,149,248 |
| Northern Mariana Islands | Northern Mariana Islands Department of Commerce, Alcoholic Beverage and Tobacco Control Division | $409,671 |
| Ohio | Ohio Department of Alcohol and Drug Addiction Services | $1,761,465 |
| Oklahoma | Oklahoma Alcoholic Beverage Laws Enforcement Commission | $619,158 |
| Pennsylvania | Pennsylvania Department of Health, Bureau of Health Promotion and Risk Reduction, Division of Tobacco Prevention and Control | $1,790,302 |
| Puerto Rico | Puerto Rico Department of Health | $701,563 |
| Rhode Island | Rhode Island Department of Behavioral Healthcare, Developmental Disabilities and Hospitals | $1,248,157 |
| South Carolina | South Carolina Department of Alcohol and Other Drug Services | $437,014 |
| Tennessee | Tennessee Department of Agriculture, Regulatory Services Division | $711,061 |
| Texas | Texas Department of State Health Services | $2,034,411 |
| Utah | Utah Department of Health, Division of Disease Control and Prevention | $552,611 |

**(Continued)**

| State | Agency | Total Awarded To Date* |
|---|---|---|
| Vermont | Vermont Department of Liquor Control | $254,840 |
| Virginia | Virginia Department of Alcoholic Beverage Control | $2,749,503 |
| Washington | Washington State Liquor Control Board | $ 1,944,427 |
| Washington, D.C. | DC Department of Health, Addiction Prevention and Recovery Administration | $596,020 |
| West Virginia | West Virginia Department of Health and Human Resources, Bureau for Behavioral Health and Health Facilities | $1,498,449 |
| Wisconsin | Wisconsin Department of Health Services, Division of Public Health, Bureau of Community Health Promotion, Tobacco Prevention and Control Program | $869,294 |
| Totals | | $62,290,316 |

\* Awards begin in FY2010 and continued through FY2011 and FY2012. This includes the initial award, any modifications made during the course of the contract and any subsequent annual award.

# APPENDIX D. SCHEDULE OF CIVIL MONETARY PENALTIES OUTLINED IN SECTION 103(C) AND (Q) OF THE FAMILY SMOKING PREVENTION AND TOBACCO CONTROL ACT

**Civil Monetary Penalties for Retailers with Approved Training Programs**

| Violation Number | Fine |
|---|---|
| 1 | Issuance of a warning letter to the retailer |
| 2 | $250 in the case of a second violation within a 12-month period |
| 3 | $500 in the case of a third violation within a 24-month period |
| 4 | $2,000 in the case of a fourth violation within a 24-month period |
| 5 | $5,000 in the case of a fifth violation within a 36-month period |
| 6 | $10,000 as determined by the Secretary on a case-by-case basis in the case of a sixth or subsequent violation within a 48-month period |

**Civil Monetory Penalties for Retailers without Approved
Training Programs**

| Violation Number | Fine |
|---|---|
| 1 | $250 in the case of the first violation |
| 2 | $500 in the case of a second violation within a 12-month period |
| 3 | $1000 in the case of a third violation within a 24-month period |
| 4 | $2,000 in the case of a fourth violation within a 24-month period |
| 5 | $5,000 in the case of a fifth violation within a 36-month period |
| 6 | $10,000, as determined by the Secretary on a case-by-case basis, in the case of a sixth or subsequent violation within a 48-month period |

# APPENDIX E. NATIONAL PUBLIC EDUCATION CAMPAIGNS CONTRACT AWARDS

## National Public Education Campaigns Support Services Solicitation

### *Full and Open—Base Contract Awardees*
- American Legacy Foundation
- Campbell-Ewald
- Draft FCB
- Grey
- Mullen
- RIESTER

### *Small Business—Base Contract Awardees*
- Better World Advertising
- Rescue Social Change Group
- Sensis Agency

## End Notes

[1] *See Centers for Disease Control.* "Fact Sheets: Smoking & Tobacco Use." www.cdc.gov/tobacco.

[2] *Ibid.*

[3] *See* "'Department of Health and Human Services Semiannual Regulatory Agenda." 78 Fed. Reg. 1579 (Jan. 8, 2013).

[4] 123 Stat. 1776, I 783 explains that the three-year time period shall commence on the first day of the first fiscal quarter following the initial 2 consecutive fiscal quarters 2010 for which the Secretary of Health and Human Services has collected fees under section 919 of the Federal Food, Drug, and Cosmetic Act. Thus, the due date for this report is Aprill, 2013.

[5] Domestic manufacturers and importers of other tobacco products not currently regulated under Chapter IX of the FD&C Act, such as cigars and pipe tobacco, are not currently assessed user fees. *See* FD&C Act Sec. 919(b)(2)(B)(iii).

[6] In specifying how to determine these assessments for listed classes of tobacco products other than cigars, Section 919 of the FD&C Act references sections of the Fair and Equitable Tobacco Reform Act of2004 (FETRA)(Pub. L. No. 108-357) (7 U.S.C. 518 et seq.) that are administered by the U.S. Department of Agriculture (USDA). Assessments for cigars would be determined separately pursuant to Section 919(b)(5).

[7] Tobacco Program Funding covers employees at CTP and other FDA employees assigned to tobacco product regulation, including in the Office of Commissioner (OC), the Office of General Counsel, HHS (OGC), and the Office of Regulatory Affairs (ORA).

[8] From the time CTP was established on June 22, 2009 until the end of that fiscal year, 22 FDA personnel were temporarily detailed to CTP.

[9] FD&C Act Sec. 905

[10] "Guidance for Industry: Registration and Product Listing for Owners and Operators of Domestic Tobacco Product Establishments." 74 Fed. Reg. 58298 (Nov. 12, 2009).

[11] FD&C Act Sec. 904(a)(l)

[12] "Guidance for Industry on Listing of Ingredients in Tobacco Products." 77 Fed. Reg. 62795 (Dec. 1, 2009).

[13] FD&C Act Sec. 904(a)(3) and Sec. 915

[14] Examples of constituents that have the potential to cause direct harm to users or non-users of tobacco products include constituents that are toxicants, carcinogens, and addictive chemicals and chemical compounds. Examples of constituents that have the potential to cause indirect harm include constituents that may increase the exposure to the harmful effects of a tobacco product constituent by potentially facilitating initiation, impeding cessation, or increasing the intensity of use of tobacco products. *See* "Guidance for Industry and FDA Staff: "Harmful and Potentially Harmful Constituents'' in Tobacco Products as Used in Section 904(e) of the Federal Food, Drug, and Cosmetic Act." 76 Fed. Reg. 5387 (Jan. 31, 2011).

[15] "Harmful and Potentially Harmful Constituents in Tobacco Products and Tobacco Smoke; Request for Comments." 76 Fed. Reg. 50226 (Aug. 12, 20 I I).

[16] "Harmful and Potentially Harmful Constituents in Tobacco Products and Tobacco Smoke; Established List." 77 Fed. Reg. 20034 (April 3, 2012).

[17] "Draft Guidance for Industry: Reporting Harmful and Potentially Harmful Constituents in Tobacco Products and Tobacco Smoke Under The Federal Food Drug and Cosmetic Act." 77 Fed. Reg. 20030 (published for comments on April 3, 2012).

[18] FD&C Act Sec. 904(d)

[19] FD&C Act Sec. 201(rr)

[20] *See* FD&C Act Sec. 910(a)(2)(A)(i)(l) and Sec. 905U)(l)(A)(i). Products commercially marketed in the United States as of February 15, 2007, are not subject to premarket review requirements. *See* also "Draft Guidance for Industry and FDA Staff – Establishing that a Tobacco Product was Commercially Marketed in the United States as of February 15, 2007." 76 Fed. Reg. 22903 (published for comments on Apri125, 2011).

[21] FD&C Act Sec. 910

[22] "Draft Guidance for Industry Applications for Premarket Review of New Tobacco Products." 76 Fed. Reg. 60055 (published for comments on Sept. 28, 2011).

[23] Characteristics are defined in section 910(a)(3)(B) of the FD&C Act as "the materials, ingredients, design, composition, heating source, or other features of a tobacco product."

[24] FD&C Act Sec. 910(a)(3)(A)(i)

[25] FD&C Act Sec. 910(a)(3)(A)(ii)

[26] "Guidance for Industry and Food and Drug Administration Staff; Section 905(j) Reports: Demonstrating Substantial Equivalence for Tobacco Products." 77 Fed. Reg. 789 (Jan. 6, 2011).

[27] FD&C Act Sec. 9050)(3)

[28] "Tobacco Products. Exemptions From Substantial Equivalence Requirements." 76 Fed. Reg. 38961 (July 5, 2011). 21 CFR § 1107

[29] On June 25, 2013, FDA announced its first decisions on new tobacco products through the SE pathway and authorized the marketing of two new tobacco products and denied the marketing of four others. FDA also announced it had formally withdrawn 136 SE Reports at the request of the applicants, and it had refused to accept 20 SE Exemption Requests because the manufacturers did not meet the requirements for such an exemption.

[30] FD&C Act Sec. 911(g)

[31] FD&C Act Sec. 911(b)(1)

[32] "Draft Guidance for Industry: Modified Risk Tobacco Product Applications." 77 Fed. Reg. 20026 (published for comments on Ap1il 3, 2012).

[33] "Guidance for Industry and FDA Staff: Use of "Light," "Mild," "Low," or Similar Descriptors in the Label, Labeling, or Advertising of Tobacco Products." 75 Fed. Reg. 32953 (June 10, 2010).

[34] FD&C Act Sec. 907(a)(4)

[35] On July 23, 2013, the United States announced that it had come into compliance with the WTO rulings. However, on August 23, 2013, Indonesia requested a special WTO Dispute Settlement Body meeting to request WTO authorization to impose countermeasures based on Indonesia's allegation that the United States has not come into compliance. The United States objected to Indonesia's request, referring the matter to arbitration.

[36] *See* U.S. Department of Health and Human Services. *Ending the Tobacco Epidemic: A Tobacco Control Strategic Action Plan.* (Nov. 10, 2010).

[37] For a more detailed list of priority research questions, see "Center for Tobacco Products, FDA: Research Priorities." *Center for Tobacco Products.* www.fda.gov/downloads/Tobacco Products/NewsEvents/UCM293998.pdf.

[38] For a complete listing of TPSAC members see "Roster of the Tobacco Products Scientific Advisory Committee." *Food and Drug Administration.* http://www.fda.gov/Advismy Committees/CommitteesMeetingMaterials/TobaccoProductsScientificAdvisoryCommittee/ ucm180906.htm.

[39] *See* FD&C Act Sec. 907(e) and (f)

[40] *FDA Tobacco Products Scientific Advisorly Committee.* "Menthol Cigarettes and Public Health: Review of the Scientific Evidence and Recommendations" (July 21, 20II). www. fda.Gov/downloads/AdvisoryCommittees/CommitteesMeetingMaterials/TobaccoProductsS cientificAdvisoryCommittee/UCM269697.pdf.

[41] On July 23, 2013, FDA issued an Advance Notice of Proposed Rulemaking (ANPRM) seeking additional information to help the agency make informed decisions about potential regulatory options it might consider, such as establishing tobacco product standards, among others, related to menthol in cigarettes. The agency also made available for public comment relevant scientific information, including the FDA's independent Preliminary Scientific Evaluation of the Possible Public Health Effects of Menthol Versus Nonmenthol Cigarettes. FDA also posted the peer reviewer comments and its response to these comments on its website. In addition, the FDA announced plans to support new research on the differences between menthol and nonmenthol cigarettes and to develop a youth education campaign focused on preventing and reducing tobacco use, including menthol cigarettes.

[42] A complete listing of TPSAC meetings is available at www.fda.gov/AdvisoryCommittees/ CommitteesMeetingMaterials/TobaccoProductsScientificAdvisoryCommittee/default.htm.

[43] FDA Tobacco Products Scientific Advisory Committee. "Summary: TPSAC Report on Dissolvable Tobacco Products." (March 1, 20 12). www.fda.gov/downloads/Advisory Committees/CommitteesMeetingMaterials/TobaccoProductsScientificAdvisoryCommittee/ UCM295842.pdf.

[44] *See* "Funding Opportunities." *Center for Tobacco Products.* www.fda.gov/AboutFDA/ CentersOffices/OfficeofMedicalProductsandTobacco/AbouttheCenterforTobaccoProducts/u cm292048.htm.

[45] See: FDA -NIH research portfolio at http:// Prevention.NIH.gov/tobacco/portfolio.aspx

[46] *See* "Scientific Evaluation of Modified Risk Tobacco Product (MRTP) Applications (August 25-26, 2011)" at www.fda.gov/TobaccoProducts/NewsEvents/ucm259201.htm; "FDA Center for Tobacco Products Research Program: Expanding the Research Base for Tobacco Product Regulation (Feb. 29, 2012)" at www.fda.gov/TobaccoProducts/NewsEvents/ ucm259201.htm; and "Tobacco Product Analysis: A Scientific Workshop (April 11-12, 2012)" at www.fda.gov/TobaccoProducts/NewsEvents/ucm288107.htm.

[47] FD&C Act Sec. 102(a)(2) of the Tobacco Control Act

[48] 75 Fed Reg. 13225 (March 19, 2010). 21 CFR Part 1140

[49] The Advanced Notice of Proposed Rulemaking was issued pursuant to Section 102(a)(2) of the Tobacco Control Act, which instructed FDA to reissue the original 1996 rule with modifications to 897.30(b), as appropriate, in light of governing First Amendment case law, including *Lorillard Tobacco Co. v. FDA,* 533. U.S. 525 (2001). Part 897.30(b) of the original 1996 rule included a prohibition on outdoor advertising for cigarettes or smokeless tobacco within 1,000 feet of a public playground, elementary or secondary school. *See* "Request for Comment on Implementation of the Family Smoking Prevention and Tobacco Control Act." 75 Fed. Reg. 13241 (March 19, 2010).

[50] FD&C Act Sec. 906(d)(4)(A)

[51] Pub. L. No. 111-154; 124 Stat. 1087

[52] *Ibid.*

[53] "Non-Face-to-Face Sale and Distribution of Tobacco Products and Advertising, Promotion, and Marketing of Tobacco Products." 76 Fed. Reg. 55835-55837 (Sept. 9, 2011).

[54] "Enforcement Action Plan for Promotion and Advertising Restrictions." 75 Fed. Reg. 60759 (Oct. 1, 2010).

[55] *See* "FDA Compliance Webinars." *Center for Tobacco Products.* www.fda.gov/Tobacco Products/ResourcesforYou/BreakTheChain/ucm220 lll.htm.

[56] 15 U.s.c. 4402

[57] "Report Potential Tobacco Product Violations." *Center for Tobacco Products.* www.fda.gov/ TobaccoProducts/ProtectingKidsfromTobacco/ucm330160.htm.

[58] 15U.S.C.Sec.l331

[59] R.J. Reynolds Tobacco Co. v. FDA, 696 F.3d 1205 (D.C. Cir. 2012)

[60] "Draft Guidance: Submission of Warning Plans for Cigarettes and Smokeless Tobacco Products." 76 Fed. Reg. 55923 (published for comments Sept. 9, 2011).

[61] *Centers for Disease Control.* "Economic Costs Associated with Smoking." www.cdc.gov/ tobacco/data statistics/fact sheets/economics/econ_facts/index.htm#costs.

In: The Tobacco Control Act ...
Editor: Gia A. Chance

ISBN: 978-1-63321-468-2
© 2014 Nova Science Publishers, Inc.

**Chapter 3**

# NEW TOBACCO PRODUCTS:
# FDA NEEDS TO SET TIME FRAMES FOR
# ITS REVIEW PROCESS*

## *United States Government Accountability Office*

## WHY GAO DID THIS STUDY

In 2009, the Family Smoking Prevention and Tobacco Control Act granted FDA, an agency within the Department of Health and Human Services (HHS), authority to regulate tobacco products such as cigarettes. The act requires that tobacco manufacturers submit information to be reviewed by FDA in order to market new tobacco products and established tobacco user fees to fund FDA's tobacco-related activities. The act represents the first time that FDA has had the authority to regulate tobacco products.

Manufacturers have raised concerns about the progress of CTP, the FDA center established by the act to implement its provisions. GAO was asked to examine CTP's review of new tobacco product submissions, responses to meeting requests, and use of funds. This report examines (1) the status of CTP's reviews of new tobacco product submissions; (2) how CTP responded to manufacturers' and other entities' meeting requests, and the length of time CTP took to hold the meetings; and (3) the extent to which FDA has spent its

---

* This is an edited, reformatted and augmented version of the United States Government Accountability Office publication, GAO-13-723, dated September 2013.

tobacco user fee funds. GAO analyzed data regarding submissions received by FDA as of January 7, 2013; reviewed data on meeting requests, spending plans, and amounts obligated; and interviewed CTP and tobacco industry officials.

## WHAT GAO RECOMMENDS

GAO recommends that FDA establish performance measures that include time frames for making decisions on new tobacco product submissions and that the agency monitor performance relative to those time frames. HHS agreed with GAO's recommendations.

## WHAT GAO FOUND

As of January 7, 2013, the Food and Drug Administration's (FDA) Center for Tobacco Products (CTP) had finished initial, but not final, review steps for most of about 3,800 submissions for new tobacco products (those not on the market on February 15, 2007). Ninety-nine percent of the submissions received by FDA were made under the substantial equivalence (SE) pathway. CTP determines whether the new tobacco product in an SE submission has the same characteristics as a predicate tobacco product (a product commercially marketed in the United States on February 15, 2007, or previously found by FDA to be substantially equivalent) or has different characteristics that do not raise different questions of public health. Initial review steps include CTP's determination of whether the new product is a type regulated by FDA and whether the submission is missing information. For most SE submissions, CTP took more than a year and a half from the date a submission was received to the date these initial steps were completed. Of the 3,788 SE submissions, 3,165 were received by FDA prior to a statutory deadline (March 22, 2011) allowing the product to be marketed unless CTP finds that they are not substantially equivalent. SE submissions received after that date cannot be marketed until CTP determines they are substantially equivalent. In late June 2013, CTP made a final decision on 6 of the 3,788 SE submissions, finding that 2 of the products were substantially equivalent and that 4 were not; the remaining submissions were still undergoing CTP review. CTP officials and manufacturers told GAO that several factors (such as CTP requests for additional information from manufacturers for submissions and having to hire and train new staff) impacted the time it took CTP to review SE submissions. While CTP is working to address these factors by, for example, disseminating information to manufacturers to improve submission quality and developing training for staff, CTP does not have performance measures that include time frames for making final decisions on submissions by which to assess its progress. Without time frames, CTP is limited in its ability to evaluate policies, procedures, and staffing resources in relation to its review process and, in turn, is limited in its ability to reasonably assure efficiency and effectiveness.

A variety of outside entities (such as manufacturers) have requested meetings with CTP to discuss new tobacco product submissions, public health activities, and other issues, and four CTP offices have received meeting requests. Those offices granted more meetings (72) than they denied (22) of all the meeting requests they received through January 7, 2013. The number of calendar days from the date a meeting was requested to the date it was held ranged from 1 to 262 days, and the averages among the four offices ranged from 51 to 97 days.

FDA spent (obligated) less than half of the nearly $1.1 billion in tobacco user fees it collected from manufacturers and others through the end of fiscal year 2012; $603 million of these user fees remained unspent and, thus, remained available to CTP. CTP spent substantially less than planned in fiscal years 2011 and 2012. CTP had planned on spending a total of $611 million for fiscal year 2012; instead, the center spent $272 million for that year. CTP officials told GAO that the time it took to award contracts contributed to the center spending less than planned. For example, CTP planned to award a $145 million contract in fiscal year 2012 for a public health education campaign, but most of that amount was not awarded until the first quarter of fiscal year 2013.

## ABBREVIATIONS

| | |
|---|---|
| AI | Advice and information |
| CTP | Center for Tobacco Products |
| FDA | Food and Drug Administration |
| HHS | Department of Health and Human Services |
| OCD | Office of the Center Director |
| OCE | Office of Compliance and Enforcement |
| OP | Office of Policy |

| OS | Office of Science |
| PMTA | Premarket tobacco product application |
| SE | Substantial equivalence |

September 6, 2013

The Honorable Richard Burr
Ranking Member
Subcommittee on Primary Health and Aging
Committee on Health, Education, Labor, and Pensions
United States Senate

Dear Senator Burr:

Tobacco use is the leading cause of preventable death, disease, and disability, and it is a significant contributor to health care costs in the United States. The Centers for Disease Control and Prevention reports that smoking and exposure to secondhand smoke account for over 440,000 premature deaths per year. In June 2009, the Family Smoking Prevention and Tobacco Control Act (Tobacco Control Act) granted the Food and Drug Administration (FDA), an agency within the Department of Health and Human Services (HHS), authority to address the concern of tobacco use by young people and to regulate the manufacturing, marketing, and distribution of tobacco products using a public health standard.[1] Under this standard, FDA regulates tobacco products as appropriate for the protection of public health while taking into account the risks and benefits of tobacco products on the population as a whole, including users and nonusers. The Tobacco Control Act requires that manufacturers of tobacco products submit information—for example, a statement of the product's ingredients and a description of the methods used for manufacturing the product—to be reviewed by FDA using this public health standard in order to introduce new tobacco products into the market after February 15, 2007.[2] The Tobacco Control Act represents the first time that FDA has had the authority to regulate tobacco products.

The Tobacco Control Act also established the Center for Tobacco Products (CTP) within FDA to be responsible for implementing the act.[3] CTP was formed in 2009—the first new center within FDA in 21 years— and it implements the act by reviewing submissions for marketing new tobacco products, enforcing prohibitions on the sale of certain tobacco products, developing and issuing regulations and guidance, engaging in public education about the risks associated with tobacco product use, and performing other activities.[4] The act also authorizes FDA to assess and collect user fees from each tobacco manufacturer and importer to be spent on only FDA's tobacco regulation activities.[5] All of CTP's activities are funded exclusively through tobacco user fees.

Tobacco manufacturers have raised concerns about CTP's progress in implementing the provisions of the Tobacco Control Act. You asked us to look at CTP's review of new tobacco product submissions, responses to meeting requests, and use of resources. This report examines (1) the status of CTP's reviews of new tobacco product submissions; (2) how CTP has responded to requests for meetings from manufacturers and other entities, and the length of time CTP has taken to hold the meetings; and (3) the extent to which FDA has spent its tobacco user fee funds. We also provide information on staffing resources for conducting reviews of new tobacco product submissions. (See app. I.)

To examine the status of CTP's review of new tobacco product submissions, we analyzed data maintained by CTP's Office of Science (OS)— the CTP office primarily responsible for conducting reviews of new tobacco product submissions—regarding all submissions received by FDA as of January 7, 2013. This included data on whether specific steps of the review process were completed for each submission, and key dates for each submission. We calculated the number of calendar days to complete key steps in the review process and the number of days a submission was pending in a particular step in the process. In addition, we reviewed relevant laws, regulations, and agency documents (such as guidance documents and draft standard operating procedures) and we viewed CTP webinars on new tobacco product submissions. We also interviewed OS officials to learn about the process for tracking and reviewing submissions, and to identify factors that contributed to the time CTP took to review new tobacco product submissions. We compared CTP's review processes against internal control standards, which specify that performance measures such as time frames and the monitoring of actual performance against measures are an integral part of operating efficiently, achieving effective results, and planning appropriately.[6] Finally, we interviewed industry representatives from manufacturers and tobacco trade associations to learn about factors that may have contributed to the time taken by CTP to review submissions.

To examine on how CTP responded to requests for meetings and the length of time CTP has taken to hold the meetings, we reviewed and analyzed data from the four CTP offices that received meeting requests from manufacturers and other entities: OS, the Office of the Center Director (OCD), the Office of Compliance and Enforcement (OCE), and the Office of Policy (OP). For each of the four offices, we analyzed data provided by officials from the office on meeting requests received as of January 7, 2013, including the date requests were received and the date meetings were held. We analyzed the data from each of the four offices separately because the data maintained by each office varied. For example, OS officials only maintain data on the date the meeting request was received by FDA while OP officials maintain data on the date the meeting request was received by FDA and by OP. We analyzed the number of meeting requests granted, denied, transferred, withdrawn, and pending. We also analyzed the number of calendar days from the date the request was received by FDA or a specific CTP office, depending on available data, to the date the meeting was held.[7] Finally, we reviewed a relevant FDA guidance document, and interviewed officials from each of the four CTP offices to learn about the processes for scheduling and holding meetings.

To examine on the extent to which FDA has spent its tobacco user fee funds, we reviewed FDA's data, including information from CTP on tobacco user fees from the fourth quarter of fiscal year 2009 through the fourth quarter of fiscal year 2012, such as the amounts collected by FDA and the amounts spent by all seven CTP offices:[8] OS, OCD, OCE, OP, Office of Management, Office of Regulations, and Office of Health Communication and Education. We analyzed these data to determine how collection related to spending over time. Further, we reviewed FDA and CTP documents, such as FDA budget justification documents, CTP's spend plan (which is used by CTP to identify its plans for spending user fee funds on staffing, acquisitions, and operational needs), and CTP quarterly reports to Congress (which describe CTP's implementation of the Tobacco Control Act provisions).[9]

We assessed the reliability of FDA data we received by reviewing related documentation, performing data reliability checks (such as examining the data for missing values), and interviewing CTP officials. After taking these steps, we determined that the data we used were sufficiently reliable for our purposes.

We conducted this performance audit from November 2012 to September 2013 in accordance with generally accepted government auditing standards. Those standards require that we plan and perform the audit to obtain sufficient, appropriate evidence to provide a reasonable basis for our findings and conclusions based on our audit objectives. We believe that the evidence obtained provides a reasonable basis for our findings and conclusions based on our audit objectives.

# BACKGROUND

FDA's authority to regulate tobacco products under a public health standard is unique among its regulatory responsibilities. CTP is the FDA center with primary responsibility for executing this regulatory responsibility, and its offices conduct work in several areas, including reviewing submissions for new tobacco products to determine if such products can be legally marketed in the United States, and responding to meeting requests from manufacturers and other entities. All of CTP's activities are funded through tobacco manufacturer user fees, as required by the Tobacco Control Act.[10]

**Table 1. Description of FDA Center for Tobacco Product (CTP) Offices**

| Office | Description |
|---|---|
| Office of the Center Director | • Provides scientific, policy, and managerial leadership and direction to the other six offices that constitute the center.<br>• Communicates agency initiatives and guidance to consumers and industry in support of public health. |
| Office of Compliance and Enforcement | • Advises center officials on compliance and enforcement issues, policies, and procedures relating to regulated tobacco products and industry.<br>• Ensures that regulated tobacco products and the manufacturers, distributors, retailers and importers of those products are in compliance with the law. |
| Office of Health Communication and Education | • Leads CTP's public education and communication activities. |
| Office of Management | • Provides administrative services to support CTP's business operations in the following areas: financial management, information technology, human resources, acquisitions, management analysis, and logistics. |
| Office of Policy | • Develops and analyzes policies to implement the Tobacco Control Act. |
| Office of Regulations | • Leads and coordinates the development and issuance of regulatory and policy documents. |
| Office of Science | • Develops and implements CTP's regulatory science framework and policies in tobacco regulatory development and tobacco product review.<br>• Implements a research agenda to meet regulatory science needs and to evaluate population and public health impact of tobacco products. |

Source: GAO summary of FDA information.

## FDA Oversight of Tobacco Products

FDA—primarily through CTP—undertakes four broad categories of activities in carrying out its responsibilities and authorities under the Tobacco Control Act:[11] (1) reviewing submissions for marketing new tobacco products and setting scientific standards for tobacco products; (2) enforcing statutory and regulatory requirements prohibiting the sale, marketing, and distribution of certain tobacco products; (3) developing and issuing regulations and guidance, conducting compliance checks, and removing violative products from the market pursuant to the Tobacco Control Act; and (4) engaging in public education and outreach activities about the risks associated with tobacco product use, and promoting awareness of and compliance with the Tobacco Control Act. CTP is organized into seven offices. (See table 1.) Within CTP, OS is the office primarily responsible for conducting reviews of new tobacco product submissions; however, OS staff duties are not limited to reviewing new tobacco product submissions.

## New Tobacco Product Submissions and CTP's Review Process

Under the Tobacco Control Act, a manufacturer may make a submission to FDA for CTP's determination of whether the manufacturer may introduce a new tobacco product to the market in the United States. CTP reviews submissions made by manufacturers through one of three pathways:

- **Substantial Equivalence (SE) pathway**: Manufacturers make a submission under the SE pathway if either (1) a new tobacco product has the same characteristics as a predicate tobacco product—that is, a product commercially marketed in the United States on February 15, 2007, or a product previously found by CTP to be substantially equivalent; or (2) the new tobacco product has different characteristics from a predicate tobacco product, but does not raise different questions of public health. There are two types of submissions made under the SE pathway—provisional and regular— that are defined by the date that the product came on the market and when the manufacturer made the submission. For provisional SE submissions, a manufacturer may market the new product that is the subject of the submission while CTP conducts its review of the submission, but for regular SE submissions, a manufacturer may not market the new product until CTP completes its review and determines that the product meets the SE requirements. (See table 2.)

- **Exemption from SE pathway**: Manufacturers make a submission under the Exemption from SE pathway if (1) the new product is a minor modification (adding, deleting, or changing the quantity of an additive) of another tobacco product marketed by the same manufacturer; (2) an SE submission is not necessary to ensure that permitting the tobacco product to be marketed would be appropriate for the protection of public health; and (3) an Exemption from SE is otherwise appropriate.
- **Premarket Tobacco Product Application (PMTA) pathway**: Manufacturers make a submission under the PMTA pathway if the new tobacco product does not meet the criteria of the SE or Exemption from SE pathways—that is, the new tobacco product is not substantially equivalent to a predicate product or is not a minor modification of an appropriate product for modification. The PMTA submission must include, among other things, full reports of investigations of health risks, and must meet the public health standard described under the Tobacco Control Act (that is, would be appropriate for the protection of public health).[12]

The Tobacco Control Act does not mandate a time frame for CTP's review of new tobacco product submissions with the exception of PMTA submissions. For PMTA submissions, the act requires CTP to issue an order stating whether the product may be marketed as promptly as possible, but not later than 180 days after FDA's receipt of a submission.[13]

CTP reviews of SE submissions—primarily conducted by OS—include three key steps:[14] (1) jurisdiction review to determine if the product is regulated by FDA, (2) completeness review to determine if the submission is missing information, and (3) scientific review to determine if the product is substantially equivalent or not (see figure 1).

The jurisdiction and completeness review steps are facilitated by OS's project managers. During jurisdiction review, project managers use a checklist to determine whether the new tobacco product is an FDA- regulated tobacco product (that is, whether it is a cigarette, cigarette tobacco, roll-your-own tobacco, or smokeless tobacco).[15] During completeness review, project managers use another checklist to determine whether the submission is missing information that OS will need for scientific review, such as the product's full brand name and a rationale for why a comparison between the new and the predicate tobacco products' characteristics should find that the new product is substantially equivalent. When project managers determine that additional information is needed to make SE determinations, OS issues administrative advice and information (AI) letters to manufacturers. Initially, CTP officials said they had given manufacturers 60 days to respond to administrative AI letters, but in April 2012, CTP began giving manufacturers 30 days to respond to an administrative AI letter.

After OS finishes these initial two steps in the SE review process, the next step is a scientific review, which involves an assessment of the product by scientists in different disciplines (such as chemistry and toxicology).[16] These scientists work to determine whether the product is substantially equivalent to a product already on the market—that is, has the same characteristics as a predicate tobacco product, or has different characteristics but does not raise different questions of public health. During scientific review, OS may issue scientific AI letters to request additional information that the scientists determine is needed to make a final determination (such as clarification of ingredients and additional testing results). In these letters, CTP officials told us that OS requests that manufacturers respond within 60 days. If OS determines that the SE criteria have been met, then CTP will issue an SE order, and the product may continue being marketed by the manufacturer (if it was a provisional SE submission) or may be legally introduced into the U.S. market (if it was a regular SE submission). If neither of these criteria is met, then CTP will issue an order that the product is not substantially equivalent and the manufacturer must remove the product from the market (if it was a provisional SE submission) or cannot introduce the product into the market under the SE pathway (if it was a regular SE submission).

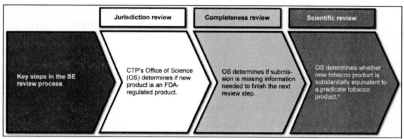

Source: GAO summary of FDA information.

Note: The steps in this figure represent key steps in CTP's review process for SE submissions. There are other steps in the review process that are not represented in this figure.

[a] A substantially equivalent tobacco product is one that CTP has found to either have the same characteristics as a predicate tobacco product (a product commercially marketed in the United States on February 15, 2007, or previously found by FDA to be substantially equivalent); or has different characteristics, but does not raise different questions of public health.

Figure 1. Key Review Steps Performed by FDA's Center for Tobacco Products (CTP) for Substantial Equivalence (SE) Submissions as of January 7, 2013.

According to CTP officials, reviews of Exemption from SE and PMTA submissions also include jurisdiction, completeness, and scientific review steps. However, the specific activities within each review step for those pathways may differ from the specific activities involved in review steps for SE submissions.

## Table 2. Types of Submissions under the Substantial Equivalence (SE) Pathway

| SE submission type | Statutory criteria for SE submission type | When manufacturer may legally market the new tobacco product in the United States |
|---|---|---|
| Provisional | • New tobacco product commercially marketed after February 15, 2007, but before March 22, 2011, and<br>• SE submission made to FDA by March 22, 2011. | May be commercially marketed unless the FDA Center for Tobacco Products (CTP) issues an order that the new tobacco product is not substantially equivalent. |
| Regular | • Does not meet the statutory criteria for a provisional SE submission. | Cannot be marketed until CTP issues an order that the new tobacco product is substantially equivalent. |

Source: GAO summary of FDA information.

Note: A substantially equivalent tobacco product is one that CTP has found to either have the same characteristics as a predicate tobacco product (a product commercially marketed in the United

States on February 15, 2007, or previously found by FDA to be substantially equivalent); or has different characteristics, but does not raise different questions of public health.

## Requests for Meetings with CTP Offices

The Tobacco Control Act does not require CTP to conduct meetings with outside entities, but CTP officials reported that they are valuable because they increase knowledge of tobacco regulation among public health groups, promote compliance among manufacturers, and clarify information needed for new tobacco product submissions. However, each CTP office follows different processes for receiving and processing meeting requests. In the event that an outside entity—for instance, a manufacturer or a public health advocacy organization—wants to meet with CTP officials, it can request a meeting in various ways. For example, manufacturers can submit written requests to the Director of OS by mail, courier, or electronically to FDA's document center. Manufacturers have requested meetings with OS to discuss their new tobacco product submissions, as well as study protocols and other scientific issues. Manufacturers, tobacco trade associations, and other entities have also proposed meetings with OS, OCD, OCE, and OP to educate CTP on tobacco industry operations (for example, current practices in tobacco product manufacturing), and to discuss industry's views on FDA's approaches to tobacco regulation (for example, industry feedback on published guidance documents). State, local, and tribal governments, as well as academic and scientific organizations, have requested meetings in order to coordinate public health efforts or share relevant knowledge. CTP officials told us that CTP follows FDA's practice not to grant meetings for which the topic of discussion is in draft guidance. Additionally, according to officials, one office within CTP may transfer a meeting request to another office within CTP in order to provide the most knowledgeable and appropriate agency officials at the meeting. However, a request may not result in a scheduled meeting.

## Tobacco User Fees

The Tobacco Control Act requires FDA to assess user fees on manufacturers of FDA-regulated tobacco products based on their market share and specifies that the tobacco user fees can only be applied toward FDA activities that relate to the regulation of tobacco products.[17] FDA bills and collects tobacco user fees from manufacturers on a quarterly basis and fees are generally collected the quarter after they are billed. For example, fees billed in the fourth quarter of fiscal year 2011 were collected in the first quarter of fiscal year 2012. The Tobacco Control Act specified the total amount of user fees authorized to be collected for each fiscal year beginning with fiscal year 2009, and authorized user fees to remain available until expended (which means that FDA may carry over user fees to subsequent fiscal years if they are not obligated by the end of the fiscal year in which they were collected).[18] (See table 3.)

All of CTP's activities, other FDA activities related to tobacco regulation (such as the tobacco-related work of FDA's Office of Regulatory Affairs and FDA Headquarters and Office of the Commissioner), and other activities such as rent are funded only through tobacco user fees.[19] According to CTP officials, 426 full-time equivalent staff in FDA were supported by the tobacco user fees in fiscal year 2012, 346 (81 percent) of which were in CTP.

**Table 3. Tobacco Control Act Authorization of Tobacco User Fees, Fiscal Years 2009 through 2019**

| Dollars in millions | |
|---|---|
| **Fiscal year** | **User fee amount** |
| 2009 | 85[a] |
| 2010 | 235 |
| 2011 | 450 |
| 2012 | 477 |
| 2013 | 505 |
| 2014 | 534 |
| 2015 | 566 |
| 2016 | 599 |
| 2017 | 635 |
| 2018 | 672 |
| 2019 and each subsequent year | 712 |

Source: GAO analysis of the Tobacco Control Act.

Note: The amounts shown are the total user fee amounts authorized to be collected by FDA for its regulation of tobacco products. Fees are collected and available for obligation only to the extent and in the amount provided in advance in appropriations acts, with the exception of user fees assessed for fiscal year 2009, which were appropriated by the Tobacco Control Act. Tobacco Control Act, § 101(b), 123 Stat. at 1826-28 (codified at 21 U.S.C. § 387s(b)-(c)).

[a] Because the Tobacco Control Act was enacted during fiscal year 2009, the $85 million authorization for fiscal year 2009 was reduced by a pro-rata amount.

# CTP Finished Initial, but Not Final, Review Steps for Most Submissions, and Lacks Time Frames for Its Review Process

As of January 7, 2013, the vast majority of new tobacco product submissions FDA received from manufacturers were made under the SE pathway. CTP has finished initial review steps (jurisdiction and completeness reviews) for most SE submissions, but CTP has not made final decisions for most submissions. For the majority of provisional SE submissions, CTP took over a year and a half to complete these initial review steps. In late June 2013, CTP made a final decision on 6 of the 3,788 SE submissions, finding that 2 of the products were substantially equivalent and that 4 were not; the remaining submissions were still undergoing CTP review. Several factors contributed to the significant amount of time it took for review of new tobacco product submissions, according to officials from CTP and tobacco manufacturers. CTP officials reported taking steps to address factors that contributed to the length of time the center has taken to review submissions, but the center has not established review time frames by which to assess progress.

## Almost All New Tobacco Product Submissions Have Been under the SE Pathway

As of January 7, 2013, nearly all new tobacco product submissions FDA received from manufacturers (99 percent) were SE submissions, most of which were provisional SE submissions. FDA received a total of 3,788 SE submissions and 23 Exemption from SE submissions from manufacturers. FDA did not receive any PMTA submissions. (See figure 2.)

As shown in figure 2, of the 3,788 SE submissions received by FDA as of January 7, 2013, 3,165 (84 percent) were provisional SE submissions and 623 (16 percent) were regular SE submissions.[20] Almost all of the provisional SE submissions were received in the second quarter of fiscal year 2011—3,115 of the provisional SE submissions were received within the 3 weeks prior to the statutory deadline of March 22, 2011. The number of regular SE submissions received in a quarter ranged from 19 (in the third quarter of fiscal year 2011) to 192 (in the third quarter of fiscal year 2012). (See figure 3.)

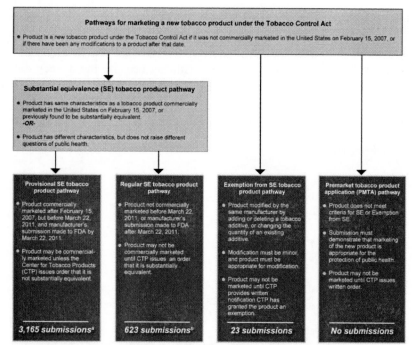

Source: GAO summary of FDA information.

Note: This figure represents new tobacco product submissions received by FDA as of January 7, 2013.

[a] Of the 3,165 provisional SE submissions, 44 were withdrawn by the manufacturer as of January 7, 2013.

[b] Of the 623 regular SE submissions, 20 were withdrawn by the manufacturer as of January 7, 2013.

Figure 2. Number of Submissions Received by FDA for Each New Tobacco Product Pathway as of January 7, 2013.

In addition to the 3,788 SE submissions, FDA received 23 Exemption from SE submissions from manufacturers as of January 7, 2013.[21] Eligibility for the Exemption from SE pathway is limited to new tobacco products that are minor modifications of an existing tobacco product (adding, deleting, or changing the quantity of an additive) already marketed by the same manufacturer. According to CTP officials, a key factor contributing to the relatively small number of submissions is that it is not common for a manufacturer to change only additives when making a change to an existing tobacco product. According to industry representatives, a key reason for the relatively small number of submissions under this pathway is insufficient guidance from CTP about what exactly constitutes a minor modification of another commercially marketed tobacco product. FDA did not include a definition of the term "minor modification" in its final rule to establish procedures for the Exemption from SE pathway because the agency did not have the experience needed to provide a useful definition.[22] In the rule, FDA stated that as it gains experience in evaluating Exemption from SE submissions, it will consider establishing a definition for minor modifications.

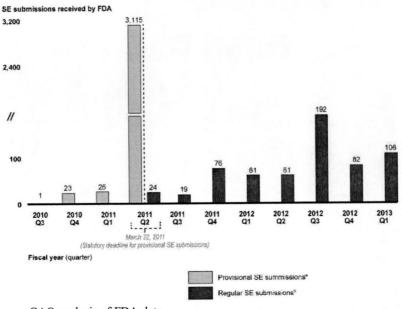

Source: GAO analysis of FDA data.

Note: This figure represents 3,788 SE submissions (3,165 provisional and 623 regular) received by FDA as of January 7, 2013. FDA did not receive any SE submission from January 1, 2013, through January 7, 2013.

[a] Provisional SE submissions are for new tobacco products commercially marketed after February 15, 2007, but before March 22, 2011. Provisional SE submissions were received by FDA by March 22, 2011. The tobacco products represented in these submissions may be commercially marketed unless the Center for Tobacco Products (CTP) issues an order that they are not substantially equivalent.

[b] Regular SE submissions are for new tobacco products not yet commercially marketed. Regular SE submissions were received by FDA after March 22, 2011. The tobacco products represented in these submissions may not be marketed until CTP issues an order that they are substantially equivalent.

Figure 3. Provisional and Regular Substantial Equivalence (SE) Submissions Received by FDA as of January 7, 2013, by Fiscal Year Quarter.

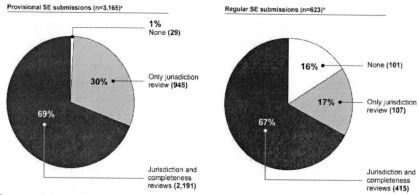

Source: GAO analysis of FDA data.

Note: This figure represents 3,788 SE submissions (3,165 provisional and 623 regular) received by FDA as of January 7, 2013, including 64 submissions withdrawn by manufacturers as of that date. Submissions withdrawn in jurisdiction review are represented in the category labeled none, and submissions withdrawn in completeness review are represented in the category labeled only jurisdiction review. Submissions withdrawn in scientific review are represented in the category labeled jurisdiction and completeness reviews.

[a] Provisional SE submissions are for new tobacco products commercially marketed after February 15, 2007, but before March 22, 2011. Provisional SE submissions were received by FDA by March 22, 2011. The tobacco products represented in these submissions may be commercially marketed unless the Center for Tobacco Products (CTP) issues an order that they are not substantially equivalent.

[b] Regular SE submissions are for new tobacco products not yet commercially marketed. Regular SE submissions were received by FDA after March 22, 2011. The tobacco products represented in these submissions may not be marketed until CTP issues an order that they are substantially equivalent.

Figure 4. Finished Review Steps for Provisional and Regular Substantial Equivalence (SE) Submissions Received by FDA, as of January 7, 2013.

CTP had not received any PMTA submissions as of January 7, 2013.[23] CTP's guidance document for the PMTA pathway states that PMTA submissions should include data from well-controlled studies demonstrating that the tobacco product is appropriate for the protection of the public health. According to CTP officials and industry representatives, one reason for the lack of submissions under this pathway may be the challenge in demonstrating that a manufacturer has met the public health standard (appropriate for the protection of public health) for the PMTA pathway. Data from such studies must address, for example, the health risks associated with the product in comparison to the health risks of other products on the market and the product's effect on the likelihood that current tobacco users will stop using tobacco products. According to industry representatives, meeting the standards under the PMTA pathway may not be feasible for some manufacturers—in particular, for small manufacturers (which are manufacturers that have fewer than 350 employees). Industry representatives reported that small manufacturers do not have the research and development resources to design or initiate clinical trials that would be needed to support a PMTA submission.

## CTP Finished Initial Review Steps for Most SE Submissions

As of January 7, 2013, CTP finished jurisdiction and completeness reviews for over two thirds of the provisional and regular SE submissions received since June 2010, but had not made a final decision on any of the 3,788 SE submissions.[24] CTP finished both jurisdiction and completeness reviews for about 69 percent of provisional SE submissions (2,191 out of 3,165), and about 67 percent of regular SE submissions (415 out of 623). Almost all of the remaining 974 provisional SE submissions and about half of the remaining 208 regular SE submissions were through jurisdiction review but not completeness review. (See figure 4.) Provisional SE submissions and regular SE submissions were pending in completeness review for as long about 1.5 years and 1 year, respectively.[25] As of January 7, 2013, CTP had not finished scientific review for any of the SE submissions.

CTP officials reported that as of late June 2013, CTP had started scientific reviews for all of the 415 regular SE submissions and 42 of the 2,191 provisional SE submissions that had finished the completeness review step as of January 7, 2013.[26] CTP officials reported that CTP began scientific reviews for provisional SE submissions in May 2013, more than a year after they began scientific reviews for regular SE submissions in March 2012 because they prioritized completeness reviews for regular SE submissions over completeness reviews for provisional SE submissions. CTP officials reported that regular SE submissions went into scientific review based on the order that FDA received submissions (which generally aligned with the order that CTP finished each submission's completeness review). CTP officials also reported that CTP prioritized scientific reviews for provisional SE submissions based on the public health impact of the new tobacco product.[27] According to CTP officials, prioritization of provisional SE submissions based on public health impact was necessary because new tobacco products in provisional SE submissions may remain on the market unless CTP finds that the product is not substantially equivalent to a predicate tobacco product.

On June 25, 2013—about 3 years after FDA's receipt of the first SE submission—CTP made a final decision on 6 of the 3,788 SE submissions. CTP concluded that the new tobacco products in two of the submissions were substantially equivalent and that the products in the four other submissions were not. These six submissions were regular SE submissions received by FDA in fall 2011 (about 1 year and 8 months prior to CTP's final decisions). For each of the two substantially equivalent products, CTP found that the new product had different characteristics than the predicate tobacco product but did not raise different questions of public health. CTP found that four new tobacco products were not substantially equivalent to predicate tobacco products due to factors such as inadequate evidence that the products to which the new products were being compared were valid predicate products and lack of complete information on tobacco product characteristics.[28]

## CTP Took Over a Year and Half for Initial Review Steps for the Majority of Provisional SE Submissions

CTP took over a year and a half from FDA's receipt of a submission through the end of initial review steps for more than half of provisional SE submissions, and 6 months for more than half of the regular SE submissions. As of January 7, 2013, the median length of time to finish initial review steps—from FDA's receipt of a submission through the end of completeness review—for provisional SE submissions was about 1 year and 9 months, and the length of time ranged from about 9 months to about 2.5 years (see figure 5). The median length of time to finish initial review steps for regular SE submissions was about 6 months, ranging from about 1 month to about 2 years (see figure 6).

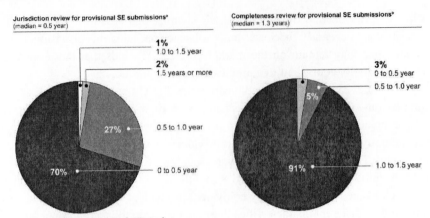

Source: GAO analysis of FDA data.

Note: Manufacturers use the SE pathway if a new tobacco product has the same characteristics as a predicate tobacco product (a product commercially marketed in the United States on February 15, 2007, or previously found by FDA to be substantially equivalent); or has different characteristics, but does not raise different questions of public health. Provisional SE submissions are for new tobacco products commercially marketed after February 15, 2007, but before March 22, 2011. Provisional SE submissions were received by FDA by March 22, 2011. The tobacco products represented in these submissions may be commercially marketed unless FDA's Center for Tobacco Products (CTP) issues an order that they are not substantially equivalent. Percentages for completeness review do not add up to 100 percent due to rounding.

[a] Jurisdiction review involves the CTP Office of Science's (OS) determination of whether the submitted product is an FDA-regulated tobacco product. This pie chart represents the length of time from FDA's receipt of a provisional SE submission to the end of jurisdiction review for 3,136 (out of 3,165) provisional SE submissions. As of January 7, 2013, CTP had not finished jurisdiction review for 29 provisional SE submissions.

[b] Completeness review involves OS's determination of whether the center requires additional information to finish the review process. Completeness review does not begin until jurisdiction review is finished. This pie chart represents the length of time from the end of jurisdiction review to the end of completeness review for 2,191 of the 3,136 provisional SE submissions through jurisdiction review. As of January 7, 2013, CTP had started but not finished completeness review for 945 provisional SE submissions.

Figure 5. Time Taken for Initial Review Steps for Provisional Substantial Equivalence (SE) Submissions.

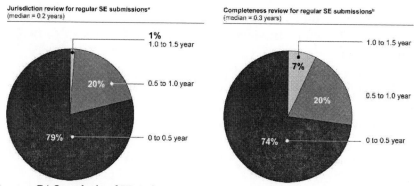

Source: GAO analysis of FDA data.

Note: Manufacturers use the SE pathway if a new tobacco product has the same characteristics as a predicate tobacco product (a product commercially marketed in the United States on February 15, 2007, or previously found by FDA to be substantially equivalent); or has different characteristics, but does not raise different questions of public health. Regular SE submissions are for new tobacco products not yet commercially marketed. Regular SE submissions were received by FDA after March 22, 2011. The tobacco products represented in these submissions may not be marketed until FDA's Center for Tobacco Products (CTP) issues an order that they are substantially equivalent. Percentages for completeness review do not add up to 100 percent due to rounding.

[a] Jurisdiction review involves CTP Office of Science's (OS) determination of whether the submitted product is an FDA-regulated tobacco product. This pie chart represents the length of time from FDA's receipt of a regular SE submission to the end of jurisdiction review for 522 (out of 623) regular SE submissions. As of January 7, 2013, CTP had not finished jurisdiction review for 101 regular SE submissions.

[b] Completeness review involves OS's determination of whether the center requires additional information to finish the review process. Completeness review does not begin until jurisdiction review is finished. This pie chart represents the length of time from the end of jurisdiction review to the end of completeness review for 415 of the 522 regular SE submissions through jurisdiction review. As of January 7, 2013, CTP had started but not finished completeness review for 107 regular SE submissions.

Figure 6. Time Taken for Initial Review Steps for Regular Substantial Equivalence (SE) Submissions.

## CTP Officials and Manufacturers Identified Several Factors That Contributed to Review Times for New Tobacco Product Submissions

Several factors have contributed to the significant amount of time it took for review of SE submissions, according to CTP officials and industry representatives. These officials identified factors such as insufficient information provided by manufacturers in submissions; the prioritization of regular SE submission reviews over provisional SE submissions; and other factors.

CTP officials told us that insufficient information from manufacturers in SE submissions has had the most significant impact on review times for those submissions. According to CTP officials, the majority of SE submissions were incomplete and required follow-up with manufacturers to obtain additional information, such as a full description of both the new tobacco product and the predicate tobacco product.

CTP officials reported that they spent significant time sending out AI letters requesting missing information from manufacturers and awaiting the manufacturers' responses. Our analysis found that administrative AI letters were associated with 2,559 SE submissions, and CTP officials told us that some submissions had more than one administrative AI letter. In these letters, CTP officials requested that manufacturers respond to requests within 60 days or 30 days. In addition, our analysis found that scientific AI letters were associated with 81 SE submissions. In these letters, CTP requested that manufacturers respond to requests within 60 days, but CTP officials reported that it had granted extensions of up to 4 months.

Industry representatives agreed that the lack of completeness of submissions had an impact on reviews, but they told us that guidance provided by CTP was neither timely nor adequate for manufacturers to provide what CTP would consider SE submissions with sufficient information. Manufacturers we interviewed said they were not able to include all information indicated in CTP guidance that was issued on January 5, 2011, for provisional SE submissions, which needed to be submitted by March 22, 2011, in order for those products to remain on the market provisionally.[29] Some industry representatives indicated that the time it took to prepare a submission was more than CTP estimated, and that the deadline for provisional SE submissions was not enough time to incorporate all of the requirements in the guidance in their submissions.[30]

Additionally, industry representatives we interviewed reported that the January 2011 guidance did not direct manufacturers to include some information by the March 22, 2011, submission deadline that CTP later requested in its September 2011 draft guidance or AI letters, such as an environmental assessment.[31]

CTP placed a higher priority on its review of regular SE submissions than on its review of provisional SE submissions, which contributed to longer review times for provisional SE submissions when compared to regular SE submissions. Specifically, according to OS officials, in the summer of 2011 CTP prioritized completeness reviews for regular SE submissions over provisional SE submissions, so resources were shifted away from provisional SE submissions. As a result of this decision—coupled with the fact that provisional SE submissions were received earlier than regular SE submissions—completeness review times for provisional SE submissions were longer than for regular SE submissions. CTP officials said that there were three reasons for placing a higher priority on its review of regular SE submissions over provisional SE submissions: (1) tobacco products in provisional SE submissions could remain on the market legally (unless and until CTP issued an order of not substantially equivalent), (2) FDA received a large number of provisional SE submissions on March 21, 2011 (the day before the statutory deadline for submitting provisional SE submissions), making it impractical to prioritize reviews by the date the submission was received, and (3) CTP required time to assess which approach to reviewing provisional submissions would be the most effective at addressing the public health burden of tobacco use.[32]

Two more factors that had a significant impact on review times were a shortage of experienced tobacco product review staff and slow IT systems, according to CTP officials. These officials reported that when they started reviews of SE submissions the center had a shortage of experienced staff and that finding qualified staff was challenging. Additionally, CTP officials said that initial training of review staff contributed to review times as new staff were unable to review submissions until receiving the necessary training. CTP officials also told us that a slow IT system impacted the rate at which project managers could enter data during jurisdiction and completeness reviews of SE submissions, which slowed down those review times.

## CTP Has Worked to Address Factors That Contributed to Review Times, but Has Not Established Time Frames by Which to Assess Progress

CTP has taken action to address the factors CTP officials identified as contributing to the significant amount of time the center has taken to review submissions. CTP has provided additional direction to manufacturers in an attempt to decrease delays due to agency requests for more information through AI letters. Specifically, it has held webinars and published frequently asked questions to provide more guidance to manufacturers that prepare submissions. Additionally, CTP officials told us that in November 2012 CTP began alerting manufacturers of upcoming scientific review of their submissions by issuing a notification to manufacturers 45 days prior to starting scientific review. According to CTP officials, this notification reminds manufacturers of the option to amend their submissions as needed prior to the start of scientific review, to facilitate higher quality submissions, and potentially avoid delays in scientific review due to the issuance of scientific AI letters. CTP also noted that it is working on a standardized form for manufacturers to use when submitting new tobacco product information for review.[33] According to CTP officials, this form may take time to develop as it will require FDA to issue regulations, but CTP officials anticipate that, when implemented, a standardized form should improve review times. To address the shortage of staff available for reviews, CTP officials told us they have increased OS staff from 12 staff in June 2010 to more than 100 staff in January 2013, including scientists and project managers involved in submission reviews. Also in 2012, CTP drafted a reviewers' guide to help train staff on aspects of the SE review process. According to CTP officials, the center plans to continue to revise its draft reviewer's guide as it further refines its new tobacco product review process. CTP officials also reported that CTP had upgraded its IT system as of early 2013, which has improved the time taken for data entry on SE submissions. They also reported that CTP plans to transition to a new IT system in late 2013.

Our analysis of data provided by CTP found that for regular SE submissions the length of time from the end of jurisdiction review through the end of completeness review improved over time. Among regular SE submissions received by FDA in fiscal year 2011 and for which CTP had finished completeness review as of January 7, 2013, the length of time from the end of jurisdiction review to the end of completeness review ranged from about 3 months to 1.5 years, with a median length of time of about 8 months.

In contrast, the length of time for these steps for regular SE submissions received in fiscal year 2012 ranged from less than 1 day to 11 months, with a median of about 2 months. CTP officials reported that actions such as hiring review staff and providing training for review staff have resulted in improved review times.

While CTP is moving forward with its reviews of SE submissions and efforts to improve review times, CTP does not have time frames for reaching a final decision on submissions. Time frames would allow CTP to evaluate its efficiency and effectiveness and help it make appropriate adjustments. Under federal standards for internal control, control activities that establish performance measures, such as time frames, and the monitoring of actual performance against measures are an integral part of operating efficiently, achieving effective results, and planning appropriately.[34] There are no time frames set by statute for the SE pathway, and CTP has not established performance measures that include time frames for making final decisions on the review of SE submissions. Although CTP officials agreed that establishing time frames would be useful for performance evaluation, CTP has not identified specific plans to establish such time frames. According to CTP officials, they have not yet established time frames because they first need to collect and analyze information about how long each review step should take. Yet without time frames, CTP is limited in its ability to evaluate policies, procedures, and staffing resources in relation to its review process and this, in turn, limits CTP's ability to reasonably assure efficiency and effectiveness. As a result, CTP is limited in its ability to determine the adjustments needed to make improvements. For example, CTP is limited in its ability to evaluate whether OS staff are performing efficiently and effectively in relation to specific review steps, and as a result, CTP may not appropriately make adjustments such as changing an individual staff member's responsibilities or increasing the number of available staff.

## CTP GRANTED MOST MEETING REQUESTS, BUT THE TIME FROM REQUEST TO DATE HELD VARIED WIDELY

As of January 7, 2013, CTP granted more meetings than it denied. The number of calendar days from the date a meeting request was received to the date a meeting was held varied widely, and CTP officials reported that logistics and subject matter contributed to these variations.

## CTP Granted More Meetings Than It Denied

As of January 7, 2013, CTP's offices had responded—granted, denied, or transferred—to over 93 percent of the meeting requests they received through January 7, 2013.[35] Based on the data provided by CTP officials from the four offices that received meeting requests from outside entities, CTP's offices responded to 108 of the 116 meeting requests received as of January 7, 2013 (see table 4). Of these 108 responses, 72 of the meeting requests were granted, 22 were denied, and 14 were transferred to another office within CTP.[36] According to CTP officials, in some cases, the CTP office denied a meeting request because the office was able to address the entity's questions by telephone and a formal meeting was no longer necessary. The remaining eight meeting requests were pending or withdrawn as of January 7, 2013. CTP officials told us that since January 7, 2013, they responded to three of the five pending meetings by granting two meetings and denying one. According to CTP officials, as of July 2013, the other two meetings were still pending because the meeting requester had not responded to CTP.

**Table 4. Meeting Requests Received by FDA Center for Tobacco Products (CTP) through January 7, 2013**

| | Number granted | Number denied[a] | Number transferred[b] | Number pending | Number withdrawn | Total requests |
|---|---|---|---|---|---|---|
| Office of Center Director | 22 | 6 | 4 | 0 | 0 | 32 |
| Office of Compliance and Enforcement | 3 | 6 | 2 | 1 | 0 | 12 |
| Office of Policy | 32 | 0 | 1 | 2 | 1 | 36 |
| Office of Science | 15 | 10 | 7 | 2 | 2 | 36 |
| **Total requests** | **72** | **22** | **14** | **5** | **3** | **116** |

Source: GAO analysis of FDA data.

[a] According to CTP officials, in some cases, the CTP office denied a meeting request because the office was able to address the entity's questions by telephone and a formal meeting was no longer necessary.

[b] The data compiled by the CTP offices did not include data on whether the transferred meeting requests were either granted or denied by the office receiving the transferred request. As a result, a transferred meeting request may also be counted as granted or denied in the office that received the transferred request.

Of the 116 meeting requests from outside entities, most (74) were requested by tobacco manufacturers. Public health advocacy organizations had the second highest number with 19 meeting requests (see figure 7).

Of the 74 meeting requests by tobacco manufacturers, 35 of the meeting requests were granted, 20 were denied, and 12 were transferred.[37] The remaining 7 meeting requests were pending or withdrawn as of January 7, 2013. For the other types of entities, most of the requested meetings were granted. For example, all 19 meetings requested by public health advocacy organizations were granted. The topics of meeting requests differed among entities. For example, CTP data indicate that tobacco manufacturers typically requested meetings about tobacco product regulation and public health advocacy organizations generally requested meetings in order to provide information to CTP that may be useful for CTP's work.

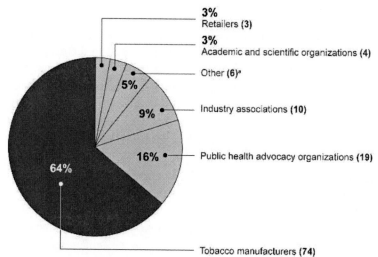

Source: GAO analysis of FDA data.

Note: This figure presents the type of entity requesting meetings with CTP offices for the 116 meeting requests received through January 7, 2013.

[a] Other entities include an animal rights organization, two federal agencies, two local, state, or tribal governments, and one entity for which CTP data did not indicate the type of entity that requested the meeting.

Figure 7. Meeting Requests Received by FDA Center for Tobacco Products (CTP) Offices, by Type of Entity.

## The Time Taken from Meeting Request to Date Held Varied Widely; CTP Reported That Logistics and Subject Matter Contributed to Variations

The number of calendar days taken from the date a CTP office received a meeting request to the date the meeting was held varied widely.[38] For example, in OP, the number of days from the date a meeting request was received to the date a meeting was held ranged from 3 days to almost five months, with half of the responses to meeting requests taking more than about 1.5 months. Further, for OCD, the number of days from the date a meeting request was received to the date a meeting was held ranged from 9 days to more than 8 months with at least half of the responses to meeting requests taking over 2.5 months. (See table 5.)

For tobacco manufacturers, the type of entity with the most meeting requests, the amount of time taken from the date the meeting request was received to the date the meeting was held also varied by office. For example, the minimum number of days from a meeting request to the date the meeting was held for OS was about a month, and the maximum was about 5 months, with half of the responses to meeting requests taking more than about 3 months. The minimum number of days from a meeting request to the date the meeting was held for OP was 3 days, and the maximum was almost 4 months, with half of the responses to meeting requests taking more than about 1.5 months.

According to CTP officials, logistics for scheduling meetings and the subject of the request contributed to the wide variation in time taken from the date of the request to the date the meeting was held. For example, OP officials said that the entity requesting the meeting may have to coordinate travel for several people across many locations in order to schedule a meeting and this coordination may contribute to a longer period of time before the meeting will take place. In addition, the subject matter of the request was another factor that CTP officials reported as contributing to the time taken by CTP offices to hold a meeting. For example, officials from OS said that CTP is a new regulatory agency and, as a result, it sometimes receives meeting requests on subject matters with which the center is unfamiliar and officials must involve many entities within both CTP and FDA to determine several things, including which office within CTP should host the meeting and what information the requested entity should prepare.

**Table 5. Calendar Days from Date Meeting Request Received to Date Meeting Held, by Center for Tobacco Products (CTP) Office**

| CTP Office (number of requests granted)[a] | Calendar Days | | | |
|---|---|---|---|---|
| | Minimum | Median | Maximum | Average |
| Office of Center Director (n=22) | 9 | 82 | 262 | 97 |
| Office of Compliance and Enforcement (n=3) | 1 | 39 | 112 | 51 |
| Office of Policy (n=30) | 3 | 45 | 150 | 52 |
| Office of Science[b] (n=12) | 22 | 86 | 149 | 79 |

Source: GAO analysis of FDA data.

[a] In general, the amounts in this table represent the number of calendar days from the date a meeting request was received by the CTP office to the date on which the meeting was held for 67 of the 72 meeting requests for which the request was granted. Data were insufficient for calculating the calendar days for the remaining meetings that were granted. All of the requests were received through January 7, 2013.

[b] For the Office of Science, the amounts represent the number of calendar days from the date a meeting request was received by any FDA office (instead of the date it was received by the Office of Science). Data maintained by the Office of Science did not include the dates that meeting requests were received by the office.

# FDA SPENT LESS THAN HALF OF THE $1.1 BILLION IN USER FEES COLLECTED

As of the end of fiscal year 2012, FDA had spent less than half of the tobacco user fees collected and CTP had spent less than planned. CTP officials reported that issues related to contracting contributed to lower than expected spending.[39]

## FDA Spent Less than Half of the User Fees Collected and CTP Spent Less than Planned

As of the end of fiscal year 2012, FDA had spent less than half of the $1.1 billion in tobacco user fee funds collected (46 percent) from fiscal year 2009 through fiscal year 2012, leaving more than $603 million (54 percent) unspent.[40] (See figure 8.) Of the almost $513 million spent during this time, CTP spent almost $468 million. The remaining funds were spent by other FDA entities, such as the Office of Regulatory Affairs.

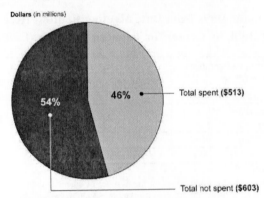

Source: GAO analysis of FDA data.

Note: FDA currently relies on the U.S. Department of Agriculture to determine a manufacturer's market share for the purpose of assessing tobacco user fees. Based on this assessment, FDA bills and collects tobacco user fees from manufacturers on a quarterly basis and fees are generally received the quarter after they are billed. This figure shows the tobacco user fees collected from fiscal year 2009 through fiscal year 2012 (which totaled about $1.1 billion), the percentage and amount of these fees spent during this period, and the percentage and amount of these fees remaining unspent at the end of this period. The total amount collected is the amount received through fiscal year 2012. The figure does not include about $62 million that was billed in fiscal year 2012 but collected in fiscal year 2013. Of the almost $513 million spent by FDA, the Center for Tobacco Products spent almost $468 million. The remaining funds were spent by other FDA entities (including the Office of Regulatory Affairs, Headquarters, and the Office of the Commissioner) and include funds spent on U.S. General Services Administration rent.

Figure 8. Total Tobacco User Fees Spent and Not Spent by FDA through Fiscal Year 2012.

In fiscal years 2011 and 2012, CTP spent less than the amounts it identified in its spend plan—that is, spent less than planned. According to CTP officials, the center's spend plan identifies plans for spending CTP's user fee funds on staffing, acquisitions, and operational needs.[41] The spend plan is based on user fee funds anticipated to be collected by FDA and user fee funds that CTP did not spend in the previous fiscal year.[42] Based on the spend plan for fiscal year 2011, all seven CTP offices had planned on spending a total of $225.4 million for fiscal year 2011, and these offices spent $106.4 million for that year.[43] CTP continued to spend less than planned for fiscal year 2012. (See table 6) CTP officials reported that based on spending through the third quarter of fiscal year 2013, the difference between the amount of planned spending and the amount of actual spending in fiscal year 2013 will be less than the differences between planned and actual spending in previous years. CTP planned to spend more than $810 million in fiscal year 2013, and as of June 30, 2013, CTP has spent or is committed to spend over $712 million.[44]

### Table 6. Center for Tobacco Products (CTP) Planned and Actual Spending, Fiscal Years 2011 and 2012

| Dollars in millions | | | | | | |
|---|---|---|---|---|---|---|
| | **CTP Non-Overhead** | | **CTP Overhead**[a] | | **Total**[b] | |
| **Fiscal year** | **Planned** | **Spent** | **Planned** | **Spent** | **Planned** | **Spent** |
| 2011 | $225.4 | 106.4 | 79.2 | 27.8 | 304.6 | 134.1 |
| 2012 | $585.0 | 245.7 | 25.6 | 26.0 | 610.5 | 271.7 |

Source: GAO summary of FDA data.

Note: Spending means obligations, including those for which expenditures have been made. The term obligation refers to a definite commitment by a federal agency that creates a legal liability to make payments immediately or in the future. In addition, amounts from CTP and overhead may not equal total due to rounding.

[a] Overhead includes information technology infrastructure and centralized funding for (among other things) furniture, office equipment, and center-wide training.

[b] This total does not include amounts planned or spent for other FDA entities and on U.S. General Services Administration rent. Other FDA entities include the Office of Regulatory Affairs, Headquarters and the Office of the Commissioner. In fiscal years 2011 and 2012, these entities spent $11.1 million and $24 million, respectively.

Specifically, six of the seven CTP offices spent less user fee funding than CTP planned for fiscal years 2011 and 2012. For example, for fiscal year 2011, CTP's Office of Health Communication and Education, OCE, and OS planned to spend about $30 million more than they actually spent; and the Office of Management was the only CTP office that planned to spend less than it actually spent—it planned to spend about $1 million less than it spent. (See figure 9.)

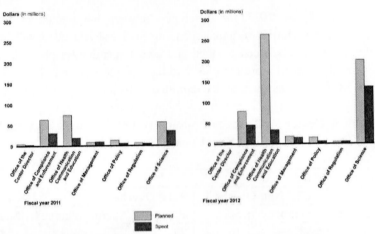

Source: GAO analysis of FDA data.

Note: Planned refers to the amount indicated in CTP's annual spend plan. Spending means obligations, including those for which expenditures have been made. The term obligation refers to a definite commitment by a federal agency that creates a legal liability to make payments immediately or in the future.

Figure 9. Center for Tobacco Products (CTP) Planned and Actual Spending, by Office, Fiscal Years 2011 and 2012.

## CTP Officials Reported That Issues Related to Contracting Contributed to Lower than Expected Spending

CTP officials told us that issues related to contracting accounted for most of the difference between the amounts spent and planned spending. Specifically, they reported that the time it took to award contracts resulted in CTP not spending the funds that the center planned to spend for a given fiscal year. For example, according to CTP officials, CTP's Office of Health Communication and Education had planned to award a $55 million contract for communications support services for part of its public education campaign for fiscal year 2011. This office also planned to award a related $145 million contract in fiscal year 2012 for a public health education campaign. However, most of the planned $200 million total was not awarded until the first quarter of fiscal year 2013.[45] CTP officials told us that both contracts were not awarded at these amounts in fiscal year 2011 or 2012 as planned because CTP and FDA spent significant amounts of time to determine the structure of the contract as FDA had never conducted a public education campaign of this magnitude.

Spending for other contracts for both fiscal years 2011 and 2012 was lower than expected for a number of reasons, according to CTP officials: fewer than expected contracts were awarded, the scope of a contract changed, or CTP was short of staff to support the work of the contract.

- For fiscal year 2011, CTP's OCE had planned to award $55 million in contracts with states to ensure compliance with tobacco regulations, but CTP awarded a total of $24 million for that fiscal year because fewer states participated than expected.
- For fiscal year 2012, CTP's OS entered into an interagency agreement with the Centers for Disease Control and Prevention to develop analytical methods and establish baseline levels of harmful or potentially harmful constituents in tobacco products for $20 million less than planned because of a change in scope of the activities for this contract.
- For fiscal year 2011, CTP's Office of Health Communication and Education entered into an interagency agreement with the National Institutes of Health to support regulatory communications activities. The agreement was $3.5 million less than initially planned because the Office of Health Communication and Education was just being established at the time and it did not have enough staff to support this joint effort. As a result, the office reduced the scope of the contract.

In addition to issues related to contracting, CTP officials said that plans to hire more staff than it did and planned management related activities that were not undertaken were other reasons why the amounts spent were lower than planned. According to CTP officials, for fiscal years 2011 and 2012, CTP had planned to hire more staff than it did and this accounted for $6 million and $10 million of the differences between amounts planned to be spent and spent, respectively. Further, according to CTP officials, lower than planned spending for other management activities (such as computer updates and planning potential reorganization) is another reason why the amounts spent by CTP were lower than planned. For example, for fiscal year 2011, the CTP spend plan included $35 million for planning associated with establishing two new offices within CTP. According to CTP officials, this amount was expected to cover contingencies, such as computer updates or management development, if they were needed. However, the officials reported that this reserve was not used because funds were available in the Office of Management to handle any issues related to the addition of these new offices.

## CONCLUSION

Four years after the Tobacco Control Act established CTP and about 3 years after the first new tobacco product submission, FDA has received about 4,000 submissions and collected over $1.1 billion in tobacco user fee funds. Although CTP has finished initial review steps for most of these submissions, as of June 2013, the center made a final decision on only 6 submissions and the time taken on reviews has been significant. Certainly, insufficient information provided by manufacturers in submissions, the prioritization of regular SE submission reviews over provisional SE submissions, and other factors have contributed to the time CTP has taken in its reviews. Yet, as CTP moves forward with its work, the lack of performance measures like time frames for reviews of SE submissions will limit CTP's ability to evaluate policies, procedures, and staffing resources in relation to CTP's submission review process and, in turn, limit CTP's ability to reasonably assure efficient operations and effective results. An entity that is limited in its ability to evaluate its performance will be hard-pressed to determine what adjustments it should make to its operations or how to plan for the future.

## RECOMMENDATIONS FOR EXECUTIVE ACTION

To improve CTP's ability to operate efficiently, achieve effective results, and plan appropriately, we recommend that the Secretary of Health and Human Services direct the Commissioner of FDA to

- establish performance measures that include time frames for making final decisions on SE submissions and Exemption from SE submissions, and
- monitor FDA's performance relative to those time frames, such as evaluating whether staff are performing reviews of these submissions efficiently and effectively.

## Agency Comments

We provided a draft of this report to HHS for comment. In its written comments, HHS agreed with our recommendations. Specifically, HHS stated that FDA will identify performance measures and time frames for regular SE and Exemption from SE review processes within 6 months of our report's publication and that FDA will monitor its progress to determine if subsequent SE reviews meet the identified time frames. In addition, HHS commented that FDA will identify performance measures and time frames for the provisional SE review process as FDA gains more experience reviewing these SE submissions. HHS further stated that based on the actual performance of meeting the identified time frames, FDA will make modifications to the review process, if appropriate, in order to meet agency objectives.

HHS also provided additional information on CTP activities in its comments. For example, HHS stated that CTP is working to reach determinations on SE and Exemption from SE submissions as expeditiously as possible, and that CTP has continued to make progress on conducting product reviews and in its process and timeliness for responding to requests for meetings with CTP offices. Regarding tobacco user fee funds, HHS commented that CTP is projecting that it will decrease the amount of unspent tobacco user fee funds to carry over at the end of fiscal year 2013 to the mid-$200 millions, which is less than half of the amount carried over at the end of fiscal year 2012. HHS also suggested that our report should include information on all user fee spending, including spending by FDA entities other than CTP. We do report total user fees spent and not spent by FDA, including spending by both CTP and other FDA entities, through fiscal year 2012. In comparing spend plans with actual spending, we reported on spending by CTP, which comprised more than 90 percent of the $513 million spent by FDA through fiscal year 2012. In reporting on CTP spending, we clearly note that other FDA entities, including the Office of Regulatory Affairs, Headquarters, and the Office of the Commissioner, spend tobacco user fee funds, and that these entities spent $11 million in fiscal year 2011 and $24 million in fiscal year 2012.

HHS also provided technical comments that were incorporated, as appropriate.

Sincerely yours,
Marcia Crosse
Director, Health Care

# APPENDIX I. STAFFING RESOURCES FOR CONDUCTING REVIEWS OF NEW TOBACCO PRODUCT SUBMISSIONS

As of January 7, 2013, the Office of Science (OS)—the only Center for Tobacco Products (CTP) office involved in all steps of reviewing new tobacco product submissions—had 124 staff members on board, and the majority of the staff (102 or 82 percent) reported spending some portion of their time reviewing new tobacco product submissions. OS has other responsibilities in addition to reviewing new tobacco product submissions, including research to meet regulatory science needs and to evaluate the population and public health impact of tobacco products. According to OS officials, of the 102 staff who reported spending time on reviewing submissions, 60 percent or 61 staff reported that in general they spent at least half of their time working on reviews of new tobacco product submissions. The remaining 41 staff reported generally spending less half of their time on reviews of new tobacco product submissions.[46] (See figure 10.)

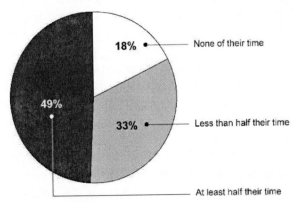

Source: GAO analysis of FDA data.

Note: This figure represents the percentage of staff that spent less than or at least half of their time working on reviews of new tobacco product submissions, as reported by 124 OS staff that were on board as of January 7, 2013. According to OS officials, specific details on how many full-time equivalent staff spent time on reviews of new tobacco product submissions were not available. In the absence of specific data, we obtained data from OS on the proportion of time (none of the time, less than 50 percent of the time, or 50 percent or more of the time) staff members in each OS position spent on new tobacco submissions, for staff on board as of January 7, 2013.

Figure 10. Center for Tobacco Products (CTP) Office of Science (OS) Staff Time Spent Conducting Reviews of New Tobacco Products.

**Table 7. Time Spent on Review of New Tobacco Product Submissions for the Center for Tobacco Products (CTP) Office of Science by Job Title**

| Time on reviews of submissions | Office of Science Job titles | | | |
|---|---|---|---|---|
| 50 percent or more | • Director, Office of Science<br>• Associate Director Regulatory Science Management<br>• Associate Director for Science Policy<br>• Medical Officer | • Regulatory Health Project Manager<br>• Director, Regulatory Science Informatics<br>• Regulatory Health Information Specialist<br>• Director, Deputy Director, Product Science | • Chemist<br>• Engineer<br>• Toxicologist<br>• Pharmacologist | • Interdisciplinary Scientist<br>• Fellow<br>• Statistician |
| Less than 50 percent | • Deputy Director for Research<br>• Special Assistant to the Director | • Conflict of Interest Specialist<br>• Health Scientist Administrator | • Psychologist/ Behavioral Scientist/ Neuroscientist<br>• Epidemiologist<br>• Social Scientist | |

Source: GAO summary of FDA information.

Note: This table shows the job titles for which CTP staff reported generally spending 50 percent or more of their time on new tobacco product submission reviews or less than 50 percent of their time (but more than 0 percent) on new tobacco product submission reviews, as reported by Office of Science staff that were on board as of January 7, 2013. The number of staff for each job titled varied from 1 to 23 staff. The job title with 23 staff was regulatory health project manager.

The amount of time an OS staff person reported spending on new tobacco product submissions varied by job title. Specifically, the 23 project managers, the OS officials responsible for coordinating the reviews of new tobacco product submissions, and 17 scientists (such as chemists and toxicologists) reported spending at least half of their time working on reviews of new tobacco product submissions. Meanwhile, the Deputy Director for Research and the Special Assistant to the Director reported spending less than half of their time on the review of new tobacco product submissions. (See table 7.)

# End Notes

[1] Pub. L. No. 111-31, div. A, 123 Stat. 1776 (2009) (hereafter, "Tobacco Control Act"). Tobacco products that FDA currently regulates include cigarettes, cigarette tobacco, roll- your-own tobacco, and smokeless tobacco products. The Tobacco Control Act enables FDA to assert jurisdiction over other tobacco products—for example, cigars, pipe tobacco, hookah, and e-cigarettes that do not make drug claims—through rulemaking. In April 2011, FDA announced its plans to issue a proposed rule to regulate other tobacco products, such as e-cigarettes, that are not currently regulated, but as of July 2, 2013, the agency had not issued a proposed rule or specified which other products it planned to propose to regulate.

[2] Tobacco Control Act, § 101(b), 123 Stat. at 1808 (codified at 21 U.S.C. § 387j(b)(1)).

[3] Tobacco Control Act, § 101(b), 123 Stat. at 1787 (codified at 21 U.S.C. § 387a(e)).

[4] In addition to the term submission, CTP uses the terms report, request, and application (depending on the new tobacco product) to refer to the package of information that manufacturers provide to FDA for review in order to legally market a new tobacco product.

[5] Tobacco Control Act, § 101(b), 123 Stat. at 1826 (codified at 21 U.S.C. § 387s). User fees are a fee assessed to users for goods or services provided by the federal government.

[6] See GAO, *Standards for Internal Control in the Federal Government*, GAO/AIMD-00-21.3.1 (Washington, D.C.: Nov. 1999) and its supplemental guide, *Internal Control Management and Evaluation Tool*, GAO-01-1008G (Washington, D.C.: Aug. 2001).

[7] We did not analyze calendar days from the date a meeting request was received to the date a response was communicated because not all of the offices maintained data on the date a response to a meeting request was communicated with outside entities.

[8] For the purposes of this report, spending means obligations, including those for which expenditures have been made. The term obligation refers to a definite commitment by a federal agency that creates a legal liability to make payments immediately or in the future.

[9] We also reviewed CTP's data on the number of staff members employed in each CTP office at the beginning and end of each fiscal year, and we interviewed officials from OS about the responsibilities and activities of the staff in their office. OS officials provided self- reported data on how OS staff spend their time.

[10] Tobacco Control Act, § 101(b), 123 Stat. at 1826 (codified at 21 U.S.C. § 387s(c)(2)(B)(i)).

[11] CTP may work with other FDA offices such as the Office of Regulatory Affairs, which conducts inspections, and other HHS agencies such as the National Institutes of Health, which conducts research, to implement the Tobacco Control Act.

[12] Tobacco Control Act, § 101(b), 123 Stat. at 1807 (codified at 21 U.S.C. § 387j). To determine whether marketing of a new tobacco product would be appropriate for the protection of public health, CTP applies standards that take into account the risks and benefits to the population as a whole, including users and nonusers of tobacco products; increased or decreased likelihood that existing users of tobacco products will stop using such products; and increased or decreased likelihood that those who do not use tobacco products will start using such products.

[13] Tobacco Control Act, § 101(b), 123 Stat. at 1809 (codified at 21 U.S.C. § 387j(c)(1)).

[14] In addition to OS, CTP officials told us that OCE participates in the SE review process by confirming that the tobacco product to which the new tobacco product in the submission is being compared meets the statutory requirements for a predicate tobacco product. A predicate product is a tobacco product commercially marketed in the United States on February 15, 2007, or previously found by FDA to be substantially equivalent, in each case, provided the product has not been removed from the market at FDA's request or has not been determined by a judicial order to be misbranded or adulterated.

[15] According to CTP officials, project managers determine whether the product (including any component, part, or accessory of the product) is made or derived from tobacco; whether it is

a drug or medical device; and whether it meets established definitions for any type of FDA-regulated tobacco product.

[16] According to CTP officials, in late 2012, CTP began issuing notices to each manufacturer about the manufacturer's submission after finishing completeness review and before beginning scientific review. According to CTP officials, the notice informs the manufacturer that its submission will be undergoing scientific review and that the manufacturer has 45 days to make any amendments to the submission. In addition, in late 2012, CTP began segmenting the review process into three phases. The first phase includes FDA's receipt of a submission, jurisdiction review, and completeness review. The second phase includes the notice sent to manufacturers 45 days prior to beginning scientific review and OCE's review to determine whether the tobacco product to which the new tobacco product in the submission is being compared meets the statutory requirements for a predicate tobacco product. The third phase includes scientific review. In this phase, CTP may issue a preliminary finding letter if the manufacturer has not provided the information needed to make a final decision. CTP issued its first preliminary finding letter in April 2013. The preliminary finding letter provides the manufacturer with 30 days to provide the missing information, and OS then makes a decision on whether the product is substantially equivalent or not substantially equivalent. In this report, we present information about jurisdiction and completeness review steps (which are in the first phase) and scientific review (which is in the third phase).

[17] Tobacco Control Act, § 101(b), 123 Stat. at 1826-28 (codified at 21 U.S.C. § 387s(b)- (c)). In addition to manufacturers, the Tobacco Control Act authorizes FDA to assess user fees on tobacco product importers. FDA currently relies on the U.S. Department of Agriculture to determine the manufacturer's market share for assessing the user fees. However, in May 2013, FDA issued a proposed rule that would require manufacturers and importers to submit information needed to calculate the amount of user fees assessed under the Tobacco Control Act. 78 Fed. Reg. 32,581 (May 31, 2013).

[18] Fees are collected and available for obligation only to the extent and in the amount provided in advance in appropriations acts, with the exception of user fees assessed for fiscal year 2009, which were appropriated by the Tobacco Control Act. For each of fiscal years 2009 through 2013, Congress appropriated the total amounts of tobacco user fees authorized to be assessed and collected under the Tobacco Control Act to FDA. The fiscal year 2013 appropriation amount of $505 million, however, was subject to a five percent reduction, as a result of the sequestration order issued by the President on March 1, 2013. Therefore, the maximum amount of fiscal year 2013 tobacco user fee collections available to FDA for obligation was reduced by approximately $25 million, to $480 million. In general, actual collections may be less than the amounts authorized and, therefore, the amounts credited to the agency's account may be less than the authorized amount.

[19] Tobacco user fees are assessed differently than FDA user fees for medical devices and human drugs. FDA assesses both application and annual fees against medical device and human drug manufacturers for certain types of applications, including premarket review, and products. Such user fees, which are standard and do not vary based on market share, pay for a portion of FDA activities related to oversight of medical devices and drugs. In contrast, tobacco manufacturers do not pay user fees with their submissions for new tobacco products; instead, they pay a quarterly fee based on their market share of FDA- regulated tobacco products. FDA relies exclusively on tobacco user fee funds to support its activities related to tobacco oversight.

[20] Of the 3,788 SE submissions, 64 (44 provisional and 20 regular) were withdrawn by the manufacturer as of January 7, 2013. According to FDA officials, manufacturers are not required to provide reasons for withdrawing submissions, and FDA does not track such information.

[21] On June 25, 2013, CTP determined that the new tobacco products in 20 of these submissions—which were received by FDA in late September 2011 through late December 2012—did not

meet the requirements for the Exemption from SE pathway. CTP officials reported that they anticipate receiving new SE submissions or PMTA submissions for the products identified in these 20 submissions. In addition, from January 8, 2013, through June 25, 2013, FDA received an additional seven Exemption from SE submissions.

[22] 76 Fed. Reg. 38,961 (July 5, 2011) (codified at 21 C.F.R. §1107.1).

[23] CTP officials also reported that no submissions were received by FDA from January 8, 2013, through June 25, 2013.

[24] FDA received the first SE submission on June 11, 2010.

[25] As of January 7, 2013, provisional SE submissions not yet through jurisdiction review were pending in that step for as long as about 2 years, and regular SE submissions not yet through jurisdiction review were pending in that step for about 1 year.

[26] From January 2013 through late June 2013, FDA received an additional 165 regular SE submissions. In addition, as CTP was conducting completeness reviews of provisional SE submissions during the time period, it determined that in some cases the provisional SE submission incorrectly identified multiple new tobacco products (instead of a single tobacco product). CTP separated such submissions and, as a result, identified an additional 382 provisional SE submissions.

[27] In June 2012, CTP established four Public Health Impact Tiers for provisional SE submissions, and in August 2012, CTP—specifically, chemists in OS—began assigning provisional SE submissions to these tiers in order to prioritize scientific reviews for products with the greatest potential to raise different questions of public health. Tier 1 includes submissions with products that have high potential for raising different questions of public health, Tier 2 is for products with moderate potential, Tier 3 is for products with low potential, and Tier 4 is for products with the lowest potential. According to CTP officials, in assigning submissions to a tier, OS chemists apply a variety of criteria, such as whether the new tobacco products that are the subject of, and the predicate tobacco products referenced in, the submissions are different product types (which would result in a Tier 1 assignment) or differ only in the way in which they are labeled (which would result in a Tier 4 assignment). CTP randomizes submissions within each tier to determine the order for beginning scientific review for submissions in the same tier.

[28] Information about these final decisions, including SE orders issued by CTP and a summary of not substantially equivalent decisions, is available at http://www.fda.gov/TobaccoProducts/Labeling/MarketingandAdvertising/ucm339928.htm (accessed July 3, 2013).

[29] U.S. Department of Health and Human Services, Food and Drug Administration, *Section 905(j) Reports: Demonstrating Substantial Equivalence for Tobacco Products* (Rockville, Md.: Jan. 5, 2011).

[30] CTP estimated the average time taken to provide required information for SE submissions at 360 hours per response, including the time to review instructions, search existing data sources, gather the data needed, and complete and review the information collection. See U.S. Department of Health and Human Services, Food and Drug Administration, *Section 905(j) Reports: Demonstrating Substantial Equivalence for Tobacco Products,* (Rockville, Md.: Jan. 5, 2011).

[31] In September 2011, CTP issued a frequently asked questions document stating that manufacturers should include an environmental assessment in their submissions. According to CTP, an environmental assessment is information provided to CTP so it can determine the environmental impact of granting an SE submission. See U.S. Department of Health and Human Services, Food and Drug Administration, Center for Tobacco Products, *Draft Guidance for Industry and FDA Staff Demonstrating The Substantial Equivalence of a New Tobacco Product: Responses to Frequently Asked Questions* (Rockville, Md: Sept. 5, 2011).

[32] CTP officials told us that while provisional SE products could remain on the market prior to CTP issuing an order, CTP would have other authorities under which it could address any immediate concerns about the adverse health impact of a specific product.

[33] In June 2013, FDA opened a docket for public comment on electronic submissions of tobacco products. Docket No. FDA-2013-N-0602-0001. Electronic Submission of Tobacco Product Applications and Other Information; Public Workshop; Request for Comments. As a result of this request for public comment and a public workshop held by CTP, CTP intends to develop a standardized form for tobacco manufacturers to make new tobacco product submissions.

[34] While we focused on the timeliness of the reviews in this report, other dimensions of an organization's performance—such as the outcomes to be achieved, quality, and cost—are equally important for evaluating overall efficiency and effectiveness.

[35] The first meeting request was received by OCD on December 16, 2009.

[36] The data compiled by the CTP offices did not include data on whether the transferred meeting requests were either granted or denied by the office receiving the transferred request. As a result, a transferred meeting request may also be counted as granted or denied in the office that received the transferred request.

[37] The data compiled by the CTP offices did not include data on whether the transferred meeting requests were either granted or denied by the office receiving the transferred request. As a result, a transferred meeting request may also be counted as granted or denied in the office that received the transferred request.

[38] We analyzed the CTP offices separately because the data maintained by each office varied. For example, OS officials maintain data only on the date the meeting request was received by FDA while OCD officials maintain data only on the date the meeting request was received by OCD.

[39] For the purposes of this report, spending means obligations, including those for which expenditures have been made. The term obligation refers to a definite commitment by a federal agency that creates a legal liability to make payments immediately or in the future.

[40] The total amount collected is the amount received through fiscal year 2012, and does not include the tobacco user fee funds billed at the end of fiscal year 2012 and collected in the first quarter of fiscal year 2013 (which as of February 28, 2013, totaled about $62 million).

[41] CTP also develops spend plans for other FDA entities that carry out tobacco-related activities (which include the Office of Regulatory Affairs, Headquarters, and Office of the Commissioner) based on discussions about the tobacco related activities that these other FDA entities will perform.

[42] User fees that have not been spent can be carried over to subsequent fiscal years.

[43] CTP did not develop a spend plan at the office or overhead level for fiscal year 2010, the first year of its operation. However, CTP planned to spend almost $212 million in fiscal year 2010, which includes overhead, and spent about $67 million.

[44] In addition, CTP officials project that they will have $256 million in unspent tobacco user fee funds to carry over to fiscal year 2014, which is less than half of the amount they carried over to fiscal year 2013. CTP officials also project that unspent funds or funds carried over to subsequent fiscal years will continue to decrease.

[45] In order to meet the guarantee of these contracts, the minimum amount was awarded in fiscal year 2012 and that amount was about $300,000.

[46] According to OS officials, specific details on how many full-time equivalent staff spent time on reviews of new tobacco product submissions were not available. In the absence of specific data, we obtained data from OS on the proportion of time (none of the time, less than 50 percent of the time, or 50 percent or more of the time) each OS position spent on new tobacco submissions, for staff on board as of January 7, 2013.

In: The Tobacco Control Act ...          ISBN: 978-1-63321-468-2
Editor: Gia A. Chance                    © 2014 Nova Science Publishers, Inc.

*Chapter 4*

# TOBACCO PRODUCTS: FDA SPENDING AND NEW PRODUCT REVIEW TIME FRAMES. STATEMENT OF MARCIA CROSSE, DIRECTOR, HEALTH CARE, GOVERNMENT ACCOUNTABILITY OFFICE. HEARING ON "EXAMINING THE IMPLEMENTATION OF THE TOBACCO CONTROL ACT"[*]

## WHY GAO DID THIS STUDY

In 2009, the Tobacco Control Act granted FDA authority to regulate tobacco products such as cigarettes. The act authorizes FDA to assess and collect user fees from each tobacco manufacturer and importer for FDA activities related to tobacco product regulation. The act also requires that manufacturers submit information—for example, a statement of the tobacco product's ingredients—to be reviewed by FDA in order to market new tobacco products. FDA reviews the products using a public health standard, taking into account the risks and benefits of tobacco products on the population as a whole, including users and nonusers. The act represents the first time that FDA has had the authority to regulate tobacco products.

---

[*] This is an edited, reformatted and augmented version of testimony presented April 8, 2014 before the House Committee on Energy and Commerce, Subcommittee on Health.

This testimony highlights and provides selected updates to key findings from our September 2013 report, entitled, *New Tobacco Products: FDA Needs to Set Time Frames for Its Review Process* (GAO-13-723). This report examined (1) the extent to which FDA spent its tobacco user fee funds, and (2) the status of CTP's reviews of new tobacco product submissions. GAO reviewed FDA data on tobacco user fees collected by FDA and spent by all of CTP's offices. GAO also analyzed CTP data on product submissions, including whether specific steps in the review process had been completed.

## WHAT GAO RECOMMENDS

In its September 2013 report, GAO recommended FDA establish time frames for making decisions on submissions. FDA plans to identify time frames in spring 2014 and implement them by October 2014.

## WHAT GAO FOUND

The Food and Drug Administration (FDA) spent (obligated) less than half of the $1.1 billion in tobacco user fees it collected from manufacturers and others from fiscal year 2009 through the end of fiscal year 2012; however, FDA's spending increased substantially in fiscal year 2013. Through December 31, 2013, FDA spent nearly 81 percent of the approximately $1.75 billion in fees collected by that time. According to officials in FDA's Center for Tobacco Products (CTP), the center established by the Family Smoking Prevention and Tobacco Control Act (Tobacco Control Act) to implement the act's provisions, the time it took to award contracts contributed to the center spending less than it had planned to spend. In fiscal year 2013, FDA was able to carry out a number of activities that were originally planned for fiscal years 2011 and 2012, such as efforts to educate youth on the dangers of tobacco use. About 79 percent ($1.12 billion) of user fees spent as of December 31, 2013, was spent by three CTP offices: Office of Health Communication and Education, Office of Science, and Office of Compliance and Enforcement.

As of January 7, 2013, CTP had finished initial, but not final, review steps for most of about 3,800 submissions it had received for new tobacco products (those not on the market on February 15, 2007). Ninety-nine percent of the submissions received were made under the substantial equivalence (SE) pathway, through which CTP determines whether the product has the same characteristics as a predicate tobacco product (a product commercially marketed in the United States on February 15, 2007, or previously found to be substantially equivalent) or has different characteristics that do not raise different questions of public health. For most SE submissions received by January 7, 2013, CTP took more than a year and a half from the date a submission was received to the date CTP's initial review steps were completed; initial review steps precede a scientific review step during which CTP determines whether the product is substantially equivalent to a predicate product. CTP made its first decisions on SE submissions in late June 2013—about 3 years after FDA's receipt of the first SE submission—and as of December 31, 2013, had made final decisions for 30 of the 4,490 SE submissions the agency had received. CTP officials stated that CTP requests for additional information from manufacturers for submissions and having to hire and train new staff impacted the time it took to review submissions. GAO also found that CTP has not had performance measures that include time frames for making final decisions on SE submissions by which to assess its progress. Time frames would allow CTP to evaluate its efficiency and effectiveness and help it make appropriate adjustments.

Chairman Pitts, Ranking Member Pallone, and Members of the Subcommittee,

I am pleased to be here today to discuss the Food and Drug Administration's (FDA) implementation of the Family Smoking Prevention and Tobacco Control Act (Tobacco Control Act). Tobacco use is the leading cause of preventable death, disease, and disability, and it is a significant contributor to health care costs in the United States. In June 2009, the Tobacco Control Act granted the FDA, an agency within the Department of Health and Human Services (HHS), authority to regulate tobacco products such as cigarettes.[1] The act requires that tobacco manufacturers submit information—for example, a statement of the product's ingredients and a description of the methods used for manufacturing the product—to be reviewed by FDA in order to market new tobacco products. FDA reviews the products using a public health standard, taking into account the risks and benefits of tobacco products on the population as a whole, including users and nonusers. The act represents the first time that FDA has had the authority to regulate tobacco products.

The Tobacco Control Act also established the Center for Tobacco Products (CTP) within FDA to be responsible for implementing the act.[2] CTP was formed in 2009—the first new center within FDA in 21 years— and it implements the act by reviewing submissions for marketing new tobacco products, enforcing prohibitions on the sale of certain tobacco products, developing and issuing regulations and guidance, engaging in public education about the risks associated with tobacco product use, and performing other activities.[3] The act also authorizes FDA to assess and collect user fees from each tobacco manufacturer and importer and specifies that the tobacco user fees may only be applied towards FDA activities that relate to the regulation of tobacco products.[4] All of CTP's activities are funded exclusively through tobacco user fees.

My statement will highlight key findings from our September 2013 report on FDA's review process for new tobacco products, and includes selected updates to the report. [5] Among other things, our report examined (1) the extent to which FDA spent its tobacco user fee funds, and (2) the status of CTP's reviews of new tobacco product submissions.

To examine the extent to which FDA has spent its tobacco user fee funds, we reviewed FDA's data, including information from CTP on tobacco user fees from the fourth quarter of fiscal year 2009 through the fourth quarter of fiscal year 2012, such as the amounts collected by FDA, and the amount spent by all of CTP's offices.[6] We also reviewed FDA and CTP documents, such as FDA budget justification documents. In addition, we obtained and reviewed updated information from CTP on tobacco user fees collected and spent, including spending by each CTP office, through December 31, 2013.

To examine the status of CTP's reviews of new tobacco product submissions, we analyzed data maintained by CTP's Office of Science (OS)— the CTP office primarily responsible for conducting reviews of new tobacco product submissions—regarding all submissions received by FDA as of January 7, 2013. This included data on whether specific steps of the review process were completed for each submission, and key dates for each submission. We also reviewed relevant laws, regulations, and agency documents (such as guidance documents and draft standard operating procedures); we interviewed OS officials to learn about the process for tracking and reviewing submissions, and to identify factors that contributed to the time CTP took to review new tobacco product submissions. We compared CTP's review processes against internal control standards, which specify that performance measures such as time frames and the monitoring of actual performance against measures are an integral part of operating efficiently, achieving effective results, and planning appropriately.[7] We also interviewed industry representatives from manufacturers and tobacco trade associations to learn about factors that may have contributed to the time taken by CTP to review submissions. In addition, we obtained and examined updated data on the number of new tobacco product submissions received by FDA as of December 31, 2013. We also discussed factors affecting time frames with CTP officials.

We assessed the reliability of FDA data we received by reviewing related documentation, performing data reliability checks (such as examining the data for missing values), and interviewing CTP officials. After taking these steps, we determined that the data we used were sufficiently reliable for our purposes.

We conducted the work for the report on which this statement is based from November 2012 to September 2013, and updated selected information in April 2014, in accordance with generally accepted government auditing standards. Those standards require that we plan and perform the audit to obtain sufficient, appropriate evidence to provide a reasonable basis for our findings and conclusions based on our audit objectives. We believe that the evidence obtained provides a reasonable basis for our findings and conclusions based on our audit objectives.

## FDA Spent Less Than Half of the User Fees Collected by the End of Fiscal Year 2012; Spending Increased Substantially in Fiscal Year 2013

FDA spent (obligated) less than half of the tobacco user fees it collected from manufacturers and others through the end of fiscal year 2012; however, FDA's spending increased substantially in fiscal year 2013. From fiscal year 2009 through the end of fiscal year 2012, FDA had collected about $1.1 billion in tobacco user fees; $603 million of these user fees remained unspent at the end of fiscal year 2012 and, thus, remained available to CTP (see fig. 1). The $513 million CTP did spend was substantially less than it had planned to spend. For example, in fiscal years 2011 and 2012, CTP spent about 45 percent of what it had planned to spend. CTP officials told us that the time it took to award contracts contributed to the center spending less than planned. For example, CTP planned to award a $145 million contract in fiscal year 2012 for a public health education campaign, but most of that amount was not awarded until the first quarter of fiscal year 2013. Spending for other contracts for both fiscal years 2011 and 2012 was lower than expected for a number of reasons, according to CTP officials: fewer contracts than expected were awarded, the scope of a contract changed, or CTP was short of staff to support the work of the contract.[8]

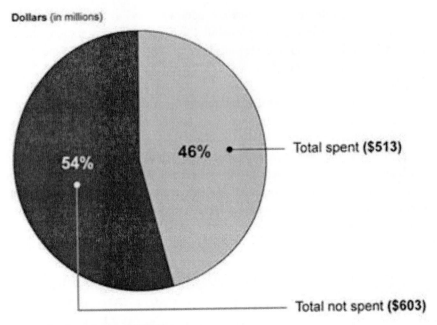

Source: GAO analysis of FDA data.

Note: This figure shows the tobacco user fees collected from fiscal year 2009 through fiscal year 2012 (which totaled about $1.1 billion), the percentage and amount of these fees spent during this period, and the percentage and amount of these fees remaining unspent at the end of this period. The total amount collected is the amount received through fiscal year 2012. The figure does not include about $62 million that was billed in fiscal year 2012 but collected in fiscal year 2013. Of the almost $513 million spent by FDA, the Center for Tobacco Products spent almost $468 million. The remaining funds were spent by other FDA entities (including the Office of Regulatory Affairs, Headquarters, and the Office of the Commissioner) and include funds spent on U.S. General Services Administration rent, other rent, and rent-related activities.

Figure 1. Total Tobacco User Fees Spent and Not Spent by FDA through Fiscal Year 2012.

The proportion of collected tobacco user fees that FDA spent increased substantially in fiscal year 2013. Through December 31, 2013, FDA had collected nearly $1.75 billion in tobacco user fees and spent nearly $1.42 billion; $332 million of these fees remained unspent (see fig. 2).

**Dollars** (in millions)

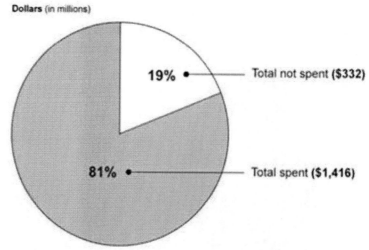

Source: GAO analysis of FDA data.

Note: This figure shows the tobacco user fees collected from fiscal year 2009 through December 31, 2013 (which totaled about $1.75 billion), the percentage and amount of these fees spent during this period, and the percentage and amount of these fees remaining unspent at the end of this period. Of the $1.42 billion spent by FDA, the Center for Tobacco Products and FDA's Office of Regulatory Affairs spent about $1.36 billion. The remaining funds were spent by other FDA entities (including headquarters and the Office of the Commissioner) and spent on U.S. General Services Administration rent, other rent, and rent-related activities.

Figure 2. Total Tobacco User Fees Spent and Not Spent by FDA as of December 31, 2013.

More than half of FDA's spending on tobacco-related activities through December 31, 2013, (61 percent) occurred in fiscal year 2013. FDA spent $868 million that fiscal year. As the contracting issues the agency encountered in the initial years of the center were addressed, FDA was able to carry out a number of activities in fiscal year 2013 that were originally planned for fiscal years 2011 and 2012 such as public health education campaigns. About 79 percent ($1.12 billion) of user fees spent as of December 31, 2013, was spent by three CTP offices: Office of Health Communication and Education, OS, and Office of Compliance and Enforcement (see fig. 3). In fiscal year 2013, CTP's Office of Health Communication and Education was responsible for the majority of the spending, which supported, in large part, its efforts to educate youth on the dangers of tobacco use.

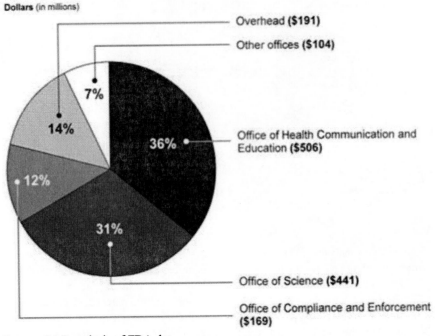

Source: GAO analysis of FDA data.

Note: This figure excludes FDA spending on tobacco-related activities in fiscal year 2009. Overhead includes U.S. General Services Administration rent and rent-related activities; Center for Tobacco Products and FDA overhead (information technology infrastructure and centralized funding for, among other things, furniture, office equipment, and center-wide training); and the tobacco-related spending of FDA headquarters and the Office of the Commissioner. Other offices include CTP's Office of the Center Director, Office of Management, Office of Policy, and Office of Regulation. Spending for the Office of Compliance and Enforcement includes spending for FDA's Office of Regulatory Affairs, which conducts inspections.

Figure 3. FDA Spending by Center for Tobacco Products Office as of December 31, 2013.

# CTP Finished Initial, but Not Final, Review Steps for Most Submissions, and Lacks Time Frames for Its Review Processes

As of January 7, 2013, CTP had finished initial, but not final, review steps for most of about 3,800 submissions for new tobacco products (those not on the market on February 15, 2007). Ninety-nine percent of the submissions received by FDA were made under the substantial equivalence (SE) pathway. Under this pathway for new tobacco products, CTP determines whether the product in an SE submission has the same characteristics as a predicate tobacco product (a product commercially marketed in the United States on February 15, 2007, or previously found by FDA to be substantially equivalent) or has different characteristics that do not raise different questions of public health. About 84 percent (3,165) of the 3,788 SE submissions received as of January 7, 2013, were provisional SE submissions—that is, they were received by FDA prior to a statutory deadline allowing the product to be marketed unless CTP finds that they are not substantially equivalent.[9] SE submissions received after that statutory deadline—called regular SE submissions—cannot be marketed until CTP determines they are substantially equivalent. In addition to submissions under the SE pathway, FDA had received 23 submissions under the Exemption from SE pathway and had not received any submissions under the Premarket Tobacco Product Application (PMTA) pathway.[10] See figure 4 for information on each new tobacco product submission pathway and the number of submissions FDA received under each as of January 7, 2013.

As of January 7, 2013, CTP finished initial, but not final, review steps for over two-thirds of the SE submissions the agency received since June 2010.[11] For most SE submissions, CTP took more than a year and a half from the date a submission was received to the date CTP's initial review steps were completed. Initial review steps include CTP's determination of whether the new product is a type regulated by FDA and whether the submission is missing information.[12] These initial review steps are followed by a scientific review, which involves an assessment of the new product by scientists in different disciplines (such as chemistry and toxicology) to determine whether it is substantially equivalent to a predicate tobacco product. As of January 7, 2013, CTP had not finished scientific review for any SE submissions—that is, had not made any decisions on SE submissions.

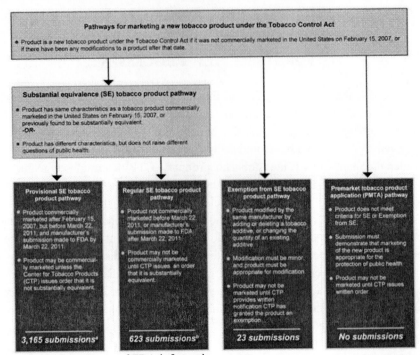

Source: GAO summary of FDA information.

[a] Of the 3,165 provisional SE submissions, 44 were withdrawn by the manufacturer as of January 7, 2013.

[b] Of the 623 regular SE submissions, 20 were withdrawn by the manufacturer as of January 7, 2013.

Figure 4. Number of Submissions Received by FDA for Each New Tobacco Product Pathway as of January 7, 2013.

CTP made its first decisions on SE submissions in late June 2013—about 3 years after FDA's receipt of the first SE submission—and as of December 31, 2013, CTP had made a final decision on a total of 30 of the 4,490 SE submissions it had received. All 30 final decisions were for regular SE submissions—FDA found 17 submissions to be substantially equivalent and 13 submissions to be not substantially equivalent to a predicate tobacco product. In addition, CTP had refused to accept 22 of the 59 Exemption from SE submissions because the submissions did not meet statutory requirements, and had made no decisions for the 4 PMTA submissions. Of the 4,490 SE submissions FDA received as of December 31, 2013, 201 submissions had been withdrawn by manufacturers; of the 63 non-SE submissions FDA received, none were withdrawn. (See table 1.)

**Table 1. Number of New Tobacco Product Submissions and Status of FDA Review, as of December 31, 2013**

| Submission type | | Submissions Initial review | | Closed review without decision (withdrawal) | Decisions Product meets criteria for marketing | Product does not meet criteria for marketing | Refuse to accept or refuse to file |
|---|---|---|---|---|---|---|---|
| | | received | completed | | | | |
| Substantial Equivalence (SE)[a] | Provisional [b] | 3,557 | 3,230 | 117 | 0 | 0 | 0 |
| | Regular[c] | 933 | 862 | 84 | 17 | 13 | 0 |
| | Total SE | 4,490 | 4,092 | 201 | 17 | 13 | 0 |
| Exemption from SE[d] | | 59 | 30 | 0 | 0 | 0 | 22 |
| Premarket tobacco product application (PMTA)[e] | | 4 | 0 | 0 | 0 | 0 | 0 |

Source: GAO summary of FDA information.

Notes: The Tobacco Control Act requires that manufacturers of tobacco products submit information—for example, a statement of the product's ingredients—to be reviewed by FDA using the public health standard in order to legally market tobacco products in the United States.

[a] Manufacturers use the SE pathway if a new tobacco product has the same characteristics as a predicate tobacco product (a product commercially marketed in the United States on February 15, 2007, or previously found by FDA to be substantially equivalent); or has different characteristics, but does not raise different questions of public health.

[b] Provisional SE submissions are for new tobacco products commercially marketed after February 15, 2007, but before March 22, 2011. Provisional SE submissions were received by FDA by March 22, 2011. The tobacco products represented in these submissions may be commercially marketed unless the Center for Tobacco Products (CTP) issues an order that they are not substantially equivalent.

[c] Regular SE submissions are for new tobacco products not yet commercially marketed. Regular SE submissions were received by FDA after March 22, 2011. The tobacco products represented in these submissions may not be marketed until CTP issues an order that they are substantially equivalent.

[d] Manufacturers use the Exemption from SE pathway for new tobacco products with minor modifications (adding, deleting, or changing the quantity of an additive) of another product marketed by the same manufacturer.

<sup>e</sup> Manufacturers use the PMTA pathway for new tobacco products that do not meet the criteria for the other two pathways. Products included in PMTA submissions can only be legally marketed after FDA issues an order permitting their marketing.

In February 2014, CTP made its first decisions on provisional SE submissions, finding products in four provisional SE submissions to be not substantially equivalent to predicate products. The agency issued orders on February 21, 2014, to stop the further sale and distribution of four tobacco products currently on the market. [13] According to FDA, the company making the SE submissions did not provide sufficient information to support a finding of substantial equivalence—for example, the company did not fully identify eligible predicate tobacco products as required for CTP to perform an SE review.

CTP officials and manufacturers told us that several factors (such as CTP requests for additional information from manufacturers for submissions and having to hire and train new staff) impacted the time it took CTP to review SE submissions. Another factor affecting review time frames was CTP's decision to place a higher priority on its review of regular SE submissions than on its review of provisional SE submissions, which contributed to longer review times for provisional SE submissions when compared to regular SE submissions. Specifically, according to OS officials, in the summer of 2011 CTP prioritized reviews for regular SE submissions over provisional SE submissions, so resources were shifted away from provisional SE submissions. CTP officials said that there were three reasons for placing a higher priority on its review of regular SE submissions over provisional SE submissions: (1) tobacco products in provisional SE submissions could remain on the market legally (unless and until CTP issued an order of not substantially equivalent), (2) FDA received a large number of provisional SE submissions on March 21, 2011 (the day before the statutory deadline for submitting provisional SE submissions), making it impractical to prioritize reviews by the date the submission was received, and (3) CTP required time to assess which approach to reviewing provisional submissions would be the most effective at addressing the public health burden of tobacco use.

While CTP has been working to address these factors by, for example, disseminating information to manufacturers to improve submission quality and developing training for staff, CTP has not had performance measures that include time frames for making final decisions on SE submissions by which to assess its progress. [14] Time frames would allow CTP to evaluate its efficiency and effectiveness and help it make appropriate adjustments. Under federal standards for internal control, control activities that establish performance measures, such as time frames, and the monitoring of actual performance against measures are an integral part of operating efficiently, achieving effective results, and planning appropriately.[15] We reported that the lack of performance measures like time frames for reviews of SE submissions will limit CTP's ability to evaluate policies, procedures, and staffing resources in relation to CTP's submission review process and, in turn, limit CTP's ability to reasonably assure efficient operations and effective results. We recommended that FDA establish performance measures that include time frames for making decisions on new tobacco product submissions and that the agency monitor performance relative to those time frames.[16] HHS agreed with our recommendation, and as of April 2, 2014, FDA officials said that they expect to identify performance measures that include time frames for the regular SE and Exemption from SE review processes in spring 2014, and to implement these performance measures by October 2014.[17]

In addition, although FDA has increased its staff and training for staff, tobacco industry stakeholders expressed concerns about whether CTP will have a sufficient number of qualified staff to review the backlog of the more than 4,000 new tobacco product submissions received as of December 31, 2013 and also review new submissions that may be made in the future, particularly if FDA asserts jurisdiction over new types of tobacco products that are not currently subject to FDA's regulatory authority. CTP officials reported that many additional staff have been and will continue to be hired and trained, and the center does not expect hiring qualified staff to be a continuing challenge for the purpose of conducting product reviews.

Chairman Pitts, Ranking Member Pallone, and Members of the Subcommittee, this completes my prepared statement. I would be pleased to respond to any questions that you may have at this time.

# End Notes

[1] Pub. L. No. 111-3, div. A, 123 Stat. 1776 (2009). Tobacco products that FDA currently regulates include cigarettes, cigarette tobacco, roll-your-own tobacco, and smokeless tobacco products. The Tobacco Control Act enables FDA to assert jurisdiction over other tobacco products—for example, cigars, pipe tobacco, hookah, and e-cigarettes that do not make drug claims—through rulemaking. In October 2013, FDA submitted to the White House Office of Management and Budget (OMB) a proposed rule to regulate other tobacco products that are not currently regulated. As of April 2, 2014, the proposed rule was still under review by the OMB and had not been issued by FDA.

[2] Tobacco Control Act, § 101(b), 123 Stat. at 1787 (codified at 21 U.S.C. § 387a(e)).

[3] In addition to the term submission, CTP uses the terms report, request, and application (depending on the new tobacco product) to refer to the package of information that manufacturers provide to FDA for review in order to legally market a new tobacco product.

[4] User fees are a fee assessed to users for goods or services provided by the federal government. The Tobacco Control Act specified the total amount of user fees authorized to be collected for each fiscal year beginning with fiscal year 2009, and authorized user fees to remain available until expended (which means that FDA may carry over user fees to subsequent fiscal years if they are not obligated by the end of the fiscal year in which they were collected). Fees are collected and available for obligation only to the extent and in the amount provided in advance in appropriations acts. For fiscal year 2014, Congress appropriated $534 million in tobacco user fees for collection and obligation—the total amount authorized under the Tobacco Control Act.

[5] GAO, New Tobacco Products: FDA Needs to Set Time Frames for Its Review Process, GAO-13-723 (Washington, D.C.: Sept. 6, 2013).

[6] For the purposes of this testimony, spending means obligations, including those for which expenditures have been made. The term obligation refers to a definite commitment by a federal agency that creates a legal liability to make payments immediately or in the future.

[7] See GAO, Standards for Internal Control in the Federal Government, GAO/AIMD-00-21.3.1 (Washington, D.C.: Nov. 1999) and its supplemental guide, Internal Control Management and Evaluation Tool, GAO-01-1008G (Washington, D.C.: Aug. 2001).

[8] CTP officials told us that fewer than expected contracts were awarded in those fiscal years because, for example, CTP and FDA spent significant amounts of time to determine the structure of public education campaign contracts.

[9] Almost all of the provisional SE submissions were received in the second quarter of fiscal year 2011—3,115 of the provisional SE submissions were received within the 3 weeks prior to the statutory deadline of March 22, 2011.

[10] Eligibility for the Exemption from SE pathway is limited to new tobacco products that are minor modifications of an existing tobacco product (adding, deleting, or changing the quantity of an additive) already marketed by the same manufacturer. New tobacco products that are not substantially equivalent or are not minor modifications of an existing tobacco product are subject to the PMTA pathway, which, among other things, requires submission of full reports of investigations of health risks. According to CTP officials and industry representatives, one reason for the lack of submissions under the PMTA pathway may be the challenge in demonstrating that a manufacturer has met the public health standard (appropriate for the protection of public health) for the PMTA pathway.

[11] FDA received the first SE submission on June 11, 2010.

[12] Our analysis of data provided by CTP found that the length of time to determine whether regular SE submissions were missing information improved over time.

[13] FDA publishes its final decisions—including the four orders for its decisions to stop the further sale and distribution of tobacco products on the market that were issued on February 21, 2014—on its website: http://www.fda.gov/tobaccoproducts/labeling/marketingand advertising/ucm339928.htm (accessed Apr. 3, 2014).

[14] The Tobacco Control Act does not mandate a time frame for CTP's review of new tobacco product submissions with the exception of PMTA submissions. For PMTA submissions, the act requires CTP to issue an order stating whether the product may be marketed as promptly as possible, but not later than 180 days after FDA's receipt of a submission.

[15] While we focused on the timeliness of the reviews in our work, other dimensions of an organization's performance—such as the outcomes to be achieved, quality, and cost— are equally important for evaluating overall efficiency and effectiveness.

[16] GAO-13-723, 39.

[17] In response to our recommendation, FDA stated that the agency will take a phased approach to implementing these performance measures and time frames, starting with regular SE submissions and Exemption from SE submissions. FDA stated that as the agency gains more experience with reviewing provisional SE submissions, it will begin to implement performance measures and time frames with respect to those submissions.

# INDEX

# PUBLIC HEALTH IN THE 21ST CENTURY

Additional books in this series can be found on Nova's website
under the Series tab.

Additional e-books in this series can be found on Nova's website
under the e-book tab.

# THE TOBACCO CONTROL ACT AND FDA REVIEW OF NEW TOBACCO PRODUCTS

## SELECTED ASSESSMENTS